The Green Home Handbook

GILLIAN MARTLEW is thirty-three and lives in Sussex. She qualified in Naturopathy (the study of natural medicine) in Canada in 1983 and now runs a private practice in Brighton. She has written four books on health and writes health-based articles for numerous major women's and natural health magazines. She broadcasts on television and radio and has a natural therapy phone-in on BBC Radio Sussex. Her interest in natural healing grew from her own ill-health in the early 1970s and the success of natural treatment, and she spent almost ten years in the USA and Canada studying and researching natural therapies. She is a member of the British Holistic Medical Association and the Society of Authors.

SHELLEY SILVER was born in New York City in 1950. She is now living in Sussex. She qualified in the biological sciences (biology, chemistry, anatomy, physiology, electron-microscopy and genetics) in New York in 1971 and ran a biological sciences learning lab for medical, dental and nursing students from 1971 to 1984 before major spinal surgery halted her career. Her interest in natural medicine grew from the desire to help her body heal without the use of drugs. She is co-author of four health books and has broadcast extensively on radio and television. She currently runs the Brighton-based Healthtec Nutrition Hotline with Gillian Martlew.

Other books by the same authors:

THE MEDICINE CHEST
THE PILL PROTECTION PLAN
STAY WELL IN WINTER

THE GREEN
HOME
HANDBOOK

A Guide to
Safe and Healthy Living
in a Toxic World

GILLIAN MARTLEW
AND SHELLEY SILVER

Fontana
An Imprint of HarperCollins*Publishers*

A FONTANA ORIGINAL

First published in Great Britain in 1991 by Fontana
an imprint of HarperCollins Publishers,
77-85 Fulham Palace Road,
Hammersmith, London W6 8JB

9 8 7 6 5 4 3 2 1

Printed and bound by
HarperCollins Book Manufacturing, Glasgow

All paper used by HarperCollins is purchased from paper
mills whose pulp is produced from sustainable forests.
The paper used in this book is produced from mechanical
pulp which uses at least 90 percent of the tree.

To Amy and William Davis
for their special inspiration and love,
and for sharing their memories.

'For the first time in the history of the world every human being is now subjected to contact with dangerous chemicals. . .'

RACHEL CARSON, *Silent Spring*, 1962

Contents

the Unavoidable – Ten-Day Detox Programme –
Protective Nutrition: What to Take – How Much
to Take – Best Dietary Sources – What Decreases
Nutrient Levels

Charts

Acknowledgements

We would like to thank everyone who became involved in this book, either directly or indirectly. We gratefully acknowledge the time and effort spent on our behalf by Steve Potts of the United States Environmental Protection Agency, and gratitude is also extended to Mary Stevens, Loveday Murley and Tim Brown of the National Society for Clean Air, Dr Wolverton of NASA, William J. Rea, M.D. of the Environmental Health Centre, Dallas, and the staff at the Sussex Postgraduate Medical Library. Special thanks to Mr Cornford of Rentokil Tropical Plants, to Alan and Jackie Gear at the Henry Doubleday Research Association, and to the Soil Association, the Health and Safety Executive and all the organizations, groups and associations who provided us with leads and information. Once again, thanks to Valerie for wading through piles of script and to the rest of the family who put up with our absence. Thanks to David for the copy of *Silent Spring* all those years ago, and to Bernard for the honest and constructive comments. And to Karin who fed us, because we would have lived on yogurt and salads if she hadn't.

Introduction

We have reached a crucial time in our occupation of the planet Earth. Many of us have woken up and realized that our world is in danger and that *we* are ultimately responsible. Unfortunately, it is often easier to continue on a familiar, albeit destructive, course because it takes less effort; it is also easy to question what one person can do to have any real ecological impact, especially since there are still so many people who seem not to care.

In the 1960s Rachel Carson stood up against chemical companies and farmers in the USA. Her book *Silent Spring* exposed the dangers of widespread chemical use on the land and the subsequent unbalancing of nature's delicate ecology. She was branded as a scaremongering, overreacting crank for her pains and it took until the early 1980s before ecological issues really began to be taken seriously.

In the desire to be 'green' and conserve the planet one aspect tends to be forgotten: chemicals which damage the earth often harm us too. We are living with hundreds of them in confined and sometimes badly ventilated buildings. We also pour them all over our gardens, throw them down drains and sanitize everything in sight with them. Given all the journalism about the planet's demise it is easy to lose sight of what is happening in our own homes. On the whole, people have only a vague idea about how household chemicals and synthetic products can affect their health – it's not in manufacturers' interests to tell them – but most people understand a little about CFCs and the ozone layer, acid rain and the destruction of forests.

The synthetic chemicals and the far-reaching fields of man-made electromagnetic radiation developed in the latter half of the twentieth century are different from anything we've ever lived with before. Until the turn of the century major changes took place as a slow, evolutionary process and there was always knowledge or experience to draw upon when questions arose or things went wrong. By producing hundreds of thousands of synthetic substances in so short a time we have created something without a history, something which only the passing of time will teach us about – and by then it may be too late to act on the information.

We are living with chemicals, including some of those used around the home, that are considered to be so dangerous that they are listed by the EEC, the Government and the Environmental Protection Agency as a danger to the environment and ourselves. We are also still living with legacies of banned chemicals, and will continue to do so for many decades.

The home and our own health are a very sensible place to start to take an active role in the making of the future of our world. This does not mean trying to live in a chemical-free environment; that would be totally unrealistic. But we *can* look after ourselves at the same time as helping to take care of the planet. As we all know, what we choose to use as consumers automatically has an influence on a far wider ecology than our immediate environment.

One of the concerns with writing a book like this is the potential to frighten people out of their wits or depress them; we have worked to achieve the opposite. Knowing what we are facing and how to avoid it or deal with the repercussions means that we have the power to make changes which will have a positive effect on our health and ultimately on the world beyond our homes. The time to use that power is now. For our own sake, and for the sake of future generations on this planet.

Nam et ipso scientia protestas est. Knowledge itself is power.

Gill Martlew

Shelley Silver

The Chemicals Problem

Chemicals and other man-made substances suspected of being health risks more often than not become officially established as hazards, but in the meantime we continue to be exposed to them until the experts find conclusive data to condemn them.

We are all caught up in a chemical rat-race. From the minute we get up in the morning to the time we go to bed (and even when we are asleep) chemicals surround our lives. We may not be aware of it, but they find their way into almost every aspect of daily living, from the water that comes out of our taps to the dyes in our clothes, from the morning paper to aspirin.

The manipulation and manufacture of synthetic chemicals has made it possible for us to alter the way we live completely – in only a few decades our lifestyles have become almost dependent on them. But we are paying the price. There are so many thousands of man-made chemicals loose in the environment now that we are being forced, by witnessing their effects, to see their dangers, not only on a planetary scale, but also in the home.

> The increased energy conserving capacity of many buildings has raised indoor chemical levels. Chemical vapours emitted by household products, furniture, carpets and pressed woods can make the chemically sensitive individual feel far worse indoors than out.

Increasing the energy conserving capacity of our homes has coincided with the introduction of more and more materials that release chemical vapours and gases. It is extremely difficult to assess indoor air quality and evaluate its precise effect on people because there are so many different factors that govern it and because there is a lack of conclusive data on many of the potential pollutants themselves. We are living with some chemical items that are believed to be unhealthy, but because it is not known *precisely* how unhealthy, it may be years before their use is restricted.

HOW CHEMICALS GET TO YOU

Chemicals enter the body by ingestion, inhalation or absorption through the skin. Those which dissolve in oils are able to penetrate the skin and enter directly into the bloodstream; other substances like lead from dust or petrol also pass easily into the bloodstream through the skin. Most chemicals are toxic if swallowed and when inhaled are again readily absorbed into the bloodstream and carried to every part of the body. Carbon monoxide and one of the breakdown products of nitrates, for example, have a direct effect on the blood by binding with haemoglobin and reducing the amount of oxygen transported to the tissues.

The nervous system, especially the brain, is very sensitive to attack by many chemicals because its functions involve chemical and electrical processes and its high fat content makes it an area where many unwanted chemicals accumulate. Certain insecticides, for instance, upset the transmission of impulses between nerves and the brain causing headaches, weakness, trembling and even collapse. Deliberately inhaling solvents can precipitate a heart attack, and the liver and kidneys, especially when diseased, can be permanently damaged by excessive exposure to certain chemicals, pesticides and heavy metals. These also have the capacity to damage genetic material, thereby increasing the possibility of cancer and birth defects.

By 1980 over 400 synthetic chemicals had been identified in human tissue. The main involvements were the blood, breast milk, liver and nervous tissue.

US Environmental Protection Agency

We are in contact with a vast assortment of chemicals but have identified only a small number of symptoms associated decisively with exposure to certain groups. The effects on the body of pollutants and chemicals, some of which react badly together, are not always obvious or immediately apparent; they can be accumulative. It may take years, even decades, before any physical sign of exposure to a chemical becomes obvious, and by then it is often difficult to link it back to a definite cause.

At present there are roughly 60,000 different chemicals in use around the world; inevitably some are used in the house and garden and in areas of work and study. A certain percentage of these are under suspicion as cancer-causing agents but the actual figures could be higher than we think. Older, more expensive and time-consuming techniques used to determine a chemical's carcinogenic potential have largely been replaced by short-term tests (SSTs) which are not necessarily reliable. SSTs take only a matter of weeks to perform and involve testing chemicals in a laboratory using bacteria and other cells grown on a Petri dish. The chemical is considered to be carcinogenic if the isolated cells are genetically damaged. The problem with this test is that chemical reactions within the body are not accounted for. Some chemicals become capable of causing genetic damage only after passing through a digestive system, or may stimulate cancerous growth by interfering with hormones.

> 'There have been many case reports of serious impact on human health due to indoor exposure to formaldehyde, to carbon monoxide and other products of unvented combustion, and to a variety of organic chemicals from consumer products. The as yet inadequately evaluated chronic exposures to imprecisely determined concentrations of a number of pollutants known to be released indoors is a matter of considerable public health concern.'
>
> *World Health Organization Indoor Air Pollutants Report, 1982*

The fact is that no one really knows how the cocktail of chemicals we invite into our lives affects long-term health, but in the short term the number of people experiencing allergic reactions is increasing, while those who may not be seriously affected by exposure to specific chemicals may still feel unnaturally tired, listless, bad-tempered, or just *ill*, especially during the winter when windows are more likely to be closed.

WHAT CHEMICALS DO TO YOU

Our ancestors were exposed to naturally occurring poisons and the stronger, healthier ones coped and adapted. But during the last five decades an overwhelming number of man-made chemicals and vast quantities of pollutants from vehicle exhausts have found their way into our lives in rapidly expanding quantities. The body is unable to build up an immunity to synthetic chemicals as it can with viruses or bacteria, but it has an inherited capacity to eliminate potentially toxic or harmful substances via the liver, kidneys, skin and other organs. The efficiency of these systems relies on genetics, general health, nutrition, and the type or volume of the pollutants.

'We live in a chemicals culture. An army of specialized molecules keeps us cleaned, disinfected, medicated, deodorized, insulated and pest-free. But white spirit is a major cause of child poisonings; woodworm treatments can cause convulsions; and dioxins — widely present in lavatory paper, tea bags, and milk cartons — are a new source of concern. . . .'

'Every year 150,000 wood preservative treatments are carried out. Many involve chemicals that have caused concern, notably pentachlorophenol (PCP), tributyl tin oxide (TBTO) and lindane. About 80 people are bringing legal actions claiming that they have suffered as a result of these substances.'

Which? Way to Health, August 1989

When exposed to chemicals the body's defence systems attempt detoxification, but in the process certain chemicals may be transmuted into other compounds. For example, one of the stages in the breakdown of trichloroethylene is the formation of several metabolic chemicals, one of which is chloral hydrate, the same substance used in medicine as a sleeping pill. In some people this stage produces physical effects very similar to those of a sedative.

We absorb, inhale and ingest many chemicals each day and physical symptoms are gradually being identified and linked to exposure to a specific chemical and accepted for what they really are. Sick building syndrome is one recognizable and classifiable manifestation of chemical exposure. It has been lifted out of the realms of 'psychological illness' since being officially recognized by the World Health Organization.

Sick Building Syndrome

The research shows that sick building syndrome is far worse in air-conditioned buildings where the natural ventilation is very poor or the air is continuously recycled. A build-up of indoor pollutants from furniture, carpets, wall panelling and stationery items, electrostatic charges from electrical equipment, high levels of carbon dioxide and bad lighting are the basis for it.

The physical signs of sick building syndrome typically include lethargy accompanied by a dull, tension headache, irritability, mental and physical fatigue, dizziness, irritation of the nose, throat and eyes, and conditions similar to hay fever, flu and asthma. Some people find that the symptoms are worse shortly after arriving in the building and improve after leaving, but there are others who begin to suffer from them as the day wears on, and continue to suffer through the evening.

Environmental Illness

Another more serious result of constant exposure to chemicals is beginning to occur amongst chemically sensitive individuals. 'Environmental illness' is a severe and debilitating condition caused by the body's reaction to chemical exposure. It is recognized by the US Environmental Protection Agency, the Occupational Safety and Health Administration and the National Academy of

Sciences who estimate that as many as fifteen percent of the American population suffer from it to some degree. There is nothing to say that the percentage isn't as high in Great Britain or anywhere else.

The understanding of environmental illness is empirical, but many clinical ecologists (practitioners who work specifically with environmental illness) theorize that continual exposure to chemicals, even at low levels, can cause an overload in the body's detoxification pathways. These can eventually become inefficient, allowing an accumulation of toxicants, especially in the brain where fat levels are high, which then affects both the immune and nervous systems. When this happens the body is unable to tolerate substances which most people consider innocuous with the result that the sufferer starts to react very severely to negligible concentrations. This condition can be irreversible.

With a classical allergy such as hay fever or an asthmatic-type reaction to house dust, the level of IgE, a protein involved in the production of antibodies, is raised significantly because the body's defence mechanisms are attempting to deal with an 'invasive' substance. Apparently this does not occur with environmental illness symptoms. This can result in such a profound effect on people suffering from it that they may be completely incapacitated by it – fainting, vomiting, unable to get out of bed or function normally at times.

Continual exposure to chemicals from foods and the environment, in conjunction with the over-use of suppressive drugs, poor nutrition and high levels of stress, can eventually tax the body's ability to process and eliminate harmful substances. Most practitioners of clinical ecology agree that avoiding unnecessary exposure to chemicals whenever possible and eating wholesome food are two of the best ways of protecting the body against environmental illness.

WHERE CHEMICALS COME FROM

Chemicals are ubiquitous and can turn up in the most unsuspected places and products. The existence of a profusion of chemicals and heavy metals present in drinking water is a well known fact, but it is less well known that forcing heated water through a shower head results in the liberation of chloroform and trichloroethylene – two noxious chemicals that are inadvertently inhaled by many people each day. Filling up a car with petrol releases numerous volatile vapours containing tetraethyl lead, 1,2-dibromethane and aromatic compounds like benzene. But perhaps the greatest concern comes from learning that manufacturers' consideration for our health can be superseded by economic considerations; depending on the quality of the product, chemicals found – unannounced – in foods and toiletries may be the same as those used in, or as, industrial and DIY products. For example:

❎ Inexpensive brands of coffee may be decaffeinated with the same solvent used in DIY products such as paint removers and synthetic turpentine, degreasers and stain removers

❎ Optical brighteners used in washing powders turn up in toothpastes, as does titanium oxide which is used in paints

❎ 2-phenylphenol, a wood preservative and masonry biocide, is used on the peel and wrappers of non-organically produced citrus fruit

❎ Nitrous oxide, an anaesthetic (laughing gas), may be used as a propellant in aerosols containing whipped cream or foams

❎ Sodium nitrate, used as a fertilizer and in the production of solid rocket propellants and explosives, is present in tobacco products and processed meats. It is also found in drinking water and vegetables grown on soils 'improved' with nitrate fertilizers

❎ Some brands of ice cream contain a vanilla flavouring formulated from an ingredient in lice killers, a binding agent made from diethylene glycol found in anti-freeze and paint strippers, substitute banana and pineapple flavours made from amyl and ethyl acetate, the solvents used in nail varnish, and nut flavours simulated by the same chemical that is a major constituent of rubber cement

❎ Numerous cosmetics and toiletries found in supermarkets contain chemicals like acetone, aldehydes, titanium oxide, ammonia and formaldehyde. These are constituents of products like paint and paint strippers, de-greasers and chrome polish.

THE DANGERS OF CHEMICAL FARMING

Farmers typically use far more pesticides than they need – and still get poor results. The crop loss suffered today is on a level with that of the beginning of the century, only now, thanks to the over-use of chemicals, many of the natural predators of pests have been eradicated and the pests themselves are becoming resistant to the assault by chemicals by breeding 'super strains'.

> The Advisory Committee on Pesticides estimates that approximately 100 tonnes of herbicides are sprayed in the UK every year. This figure does not include illegal spraying or dumping.

Lettuces and peas may receive up to ten applications of different chemicals from the time they are planted until harvest. In 1989 a farm workers' association in the USA warned people not to eat grapes because they were treated with over a hundred different pesticides that could not be washed off. Also in the USA, 1400 people were temporarily poisoned by watermelons that were found to be tainted with the pesticide aldicarb. This chemical is permitted for use on crops and foods which will be processed before eating; in the case of the watermelons it had been used illegally in an attempt to increase the yield. The watermelon contamination was discovered because aldicarb happens to be acutely toxic and causes an immediate physical reaction. A worrying aspect is that had the chemical been carcinogenic rather than toxic, no one would have known about the excessive chemical ingestion.

Out of the 1200 'inert' ingredients in pesticides only 300 are considered safe; 100 are known to be dangerous and the risks attached to the remaining 800 are unknown. 'Inert' ingredients do not have to be listed on labels.

It may take years to ban a toxic substance. During that time consumers continue to be exposed to danger while chemical companies continue to reap the financial benefits – until forced to withdraw the product from the market. In the USA pesticide manufacturers go through protracted appeals before the Environmental Protection Agency can ban a chemical. When a ban is issued the pesticide law requires the EPA to reimburse pesticide manufacturers for unsold stock.

The 'green revolution', now taken to mean the preservation of the environment and the planet, had a completely different meaning in the 1940s and 50s. In America the 1940s saw the beginning of the widespread use of chemical fertilizers and pesticides. The agricultural establishment was prompted to herald the arrival of a 'green revolution' where super hardy crops, impervious to insect pests, could be grown in unending abundance. Four decades later, in the new green revolution, many artificial fertilizers and pesticides have turned out to be highly dangerous to humans and wildlife and exceptionally persistent in the environment. Banning chemicals like DDT has not eliminated the problem because they can remain in an active state for years, even decades.

DDT (dichlorodiphenyltrichloroethane) was created by a German chemist in 1874 and remained unknown until Swiss scientists perfected it as an insecticide and introduced it to the world in 1942. It was used first in experiments on Swiss potato crops which were being ravaged by the Colorado beetle, and it proved highly effective during World War II for preventing the outbreak of typhus and cholera. To this end it was sprayed in powder form on American troops, their prisoners and civil populations. It almost eradicated mosquitos carrying malaria on the South Pacific islands and understandably seemed like a miracle. For many years it was sprayed into nearly every corner of the world.

Evidence of DDT's possible dangers surfaced in scientific and medical journals from time to time; for instance, in July 1945 the

British Medical Journal published the results of a study in which DDT applied directly to the skin had caused symptoms of chronic tiredness, irritability, ambiguous body pains and feelings of mental incompetence. DDT remained in use for many more years.

In Britain the use of DDT began to be phased out in 1974, but it still continues to infiltrate the food chain and will do so for years to come. It is stored in body fat, and under conditions of physiological need or stress fat released into the bloodstream is accompanied by stored DDT. Sudden weight loss from illness or dieting can saturate the tissues with this poison and cause symptoms ranging from uncontrollable tremors to loss of appetite.

The main pesticides developed to replace DDT were of the same chemical family, chlorinated hydrocarbons, and included lindane (only gamma HCH lindane is now permitted for use within the EEC), chlordane (now illegal for public sale in Britain), and dieldrin (which has been totally banned since March 1989). These and many routinely used chemicals appear on the EEC List I 'Black List' of chemicals 'considered to be so toxic, persistent or bio-accumulative in the environment that steps should be taken to eliminate pollution by them'. They also appear on the Government's chemical 'Red List'.

Mercury is a powerful fungicide which was used widely in the USA. In 1970 American farmers sprayed 800,000 pounds (over 363,000 kilograms) of mercury pesticides over millions of acres of farmland and planted tons of seeds coated with a mercury-based fungicide. This was believed to be safe, as was the dumping of mercury compounds into oceans and waterways. Growing data on mercury's cumulative and teratogenic dangers, and evidence that mercury was being taken up in the aquatic food chain, concentrating in large fish like tuna and swordfish, and numerous human tragedies, including the mass mercury poisoning in the Japanese village of Minamata, prompted the EPA to ban the production of virtually all mercury pesticides in February 1976. Mercury takes years to break down in the environment and is still present in the aquatic food chain.

WHO'S GOING TO PROTECT US?

Virtually all 'hazardous pollutants' controlled in the last few decades have only been eventually tackled by the government because of sustained consumer pressure. Examples include lead in petrol and paint, asbestos in the workplace, DDT and other organochlorine pesticides, and mercury.

'Environmental Health Hazards', Which? April 1989

The by-products of some chemicals can be as toxic and persistent as the chemicals themselves. 2,4,5-T, the infamous 'agent orange' defoliant used in Vietnam, is contaminated with dioxin, an exceptionally toxic chemical in its own right. The British Government has not recognized grounds to ban 2,4,5-T and at the time of writing it is still sold to the householder in a product called Kilnet. British Rail and Forestry Commission workers refuse to handle it and over ninety local councils have banned its use. It is banned in West Germany, Japan, Colombia, Guatemala, Finland, India, the Netherlands, Italy, Sweden and Thailand. In the USA it was banned by the Environmental Protection Agency in 1973. Dioxins are some of the most pernicious and harmful compounds released into the environment and are extremely persistent.

There is always a latency period between a chemical's introduction to the market and the appearance of toxicological data based on human exposure. In some cases it has been decades before overwhelming evidence of a chemical's hazards are acted upon. Although some of the seriously dangerous chemicals have eventually been banned or phased out there are still products in daily use containing chemicals that obviously do not belong in our homes or the environment. 2,4,5-T, formaldehyde, paraquat, diquat and numerous solvents are just a few examples.

In the USA the 'Freedom of Information Act' enables consumers to gain access to information on chemicals and consumer products. In the UK enquiries to chemical companies are frequently referred to government offices which either have no data or will not release it due to its 'secret' classification.

It is becoming imperative to find out which chemicals we are exposed to on a daily basis and to take steps to eliminate those which threaten our health. It is obvious by now that no one is going to do it for us, at least not until the situation becomes critical. Every one of us is a guinea pig in an immense chemical experiment and our health is in the hands of a bureaucracy which operates in a time warp. But there are many things we can do to change this.

Avoiding Chemicals in the Home

It is only comparatively recently in our evolution that we have shut ourselves away from the elements. As a result exposure to fresh air has diminished while exposure to chemicals has increased. Up to ninety percent of us spend at least seventy-five percent of our time in buildings and vehicles.

Toxic chemicals and pollutants are not only in the air outside the home, they are also in the air *in* our homes. American statistics reveal that the environment inside buildings is often more polluted than the air outside, and as more energy-saving measures are used ventilation is decreasing and the number of sources of indoor pollution increasing. Carpets, electrical equipment, paints and DIY products, aerosols, clothes, plastic items, fabrics, chipboard, bedding and thousands of common household items are manufactured using volatile chemicals, some of which release fumes into our indoor air for months, even years. Most consumers have no idea that this is happening.

Many household cleaners and DIY products are sold without a clear description of their chemical ingredients and, again, most consumers are unaware of this. There is only a legal requirement to carry contents details on solvents, cleaning and DIY merchandise when an item is above a certain size, or if it is to be used commercially. Even so, manufacturers are still allowed to keep some ingredients in their products secret. Allegedly this protects them from competitors who may try to copy the 'recipe' and create a rival product, but this is a blanket excuse for secrecy; laboratory analysis techniques and computers have made it possible to duplicate almost any chemical compound. It is also claimed that the public may panic if they are told what chemicals they are using without understanding the chemistry behind them, and that products containing certain chemicals are safe as long as the instructions are followed. It is well known in the medical profession that a high proportion of prescription instructions are ignored or misread, and the same may be true for potentially harmful household chemicals.

> Safety standards are set for single chemical exposure based on the assumption that the person using the chemical in question is adult, aged between eighteen and sixty, is in reasonable health and will be exposed for up to eight hours a day.

It is reasonable to assume that there are specific safety standards to protect consumers from hazardous chemicals, but these may fall short, possibly from lack of care on the part of the consumer, or because the individual is particularly sensitive to a specific chemical, or if chemicals have been inadvertently mixed (see Chart 3.3 in Chapter 3). The establishment of chemical safety standards is based on findings from experimental settings, but actual exposure may often be far greater in a domestic situation. Spending a winter weekend in the house catching up with DIY projects could expose members of the family to much higher and more prolonged levels than recommended of *several* chemicals. Children, the elderly and the frail are the most likely to be vulnerable to toxic effects which may not have been taken into account in safety tests.

> Babies and small children are more vulnerable to chemical toxicity than adults because of their size, and also because respiration and metabolic rates are faster and pollutants become concentrated in the body more rapidly. Many pollutants are heavier than air and accumulate at lower levels where young children breathe.

Chemicals may react together to produce another possibly *more* harmful substance. There are many chemical compounds which produce vapours that are released into the air. There are so many chemical-based household items which can emit toxic vapours that it is impossible to predict the levels and types of chemicals present in the air in the average building, or indeed what possible effect these may have on health. Most available data is based on single chemical exposure and it is not really possible to know for certain whether the minor or long-term health problems people are suffering are a result of chemical exposure. But clues are arising, one of which is the increase in illnesses like M.E. and tenacious viruses which are not being tackled effectively by the immune system. Perpetual exposure to pollutants and toxicants is known to weaken the immune response.

HOW TO USE THIS SECTION

The information in this chapter concerns chemicals and toxicants that may contaminate indoor air. Garden chemicals and products most likely to be used outside the home are documented in Chapter 4. Although specific nutritional information is included where appropriate in this section, broader information appears in Chapter 7. For more details about alternative or safer products use Chapter 8 as a guide. 'Recipes' for home-made alternatives to some commercial products appear at the end of this chapter.

In order to access information there are two avenues to follow. If you are looking up a particular chemical, scan the alphabetical Chemical Data Sheets which follow the Chemical Index. If you wish to find out which chemicals are contained in certain products, use the Chemical Index which will guide you to the appropriate entry in the Chemical Data Sheets. For instance if you look up **flame resistant fabric** in the Chemical Index you will be directed to the section on **formaldehyde** in the Data Sheets. Similarly, under the entry for formaldehyde in the Data Sheets there will be a list of all its sources, one of which is flame resistant fabric. Within the Chemical Index and the Data Sheets, chemicals or products that are listed in more detail elsewhere in the chapter will appear in **bold** print. Unfamiliar terms can be found in the glossary.

CHEMICAL INDEX

It is important to bear in mind that using a product containing a particular chemical will not automatically expose you or family members to toxic or dangerous levels of these substances. In most cases the symptoms listed have been taken from data based on extreme exposure and it is likely that side effects will be experienced only by extremely sensitive individuals or those exposed to high or continuous levels.

Item	Chemicals
Additives, food	aluminium
Adhesives	formaldehyde, toluene, trichloroethylene, 1,1,1-trichloroethane
Aerosol propellants	CFCs
Air conditioners	CFCs
Air pollution	aldehydes, aluminium, asbestos, formaldehyde, lead, smog
Aluminium foil	aluminium
Antacids	aluminium
Antifreeze	diethylene glycol
Antiperspirants/deodorants	aluminium, formaldehyde
Asthma inhalers	CFCs
Baby pants	plastics (polyvinyl chloride – PVC)
Baking powder	aluminium
Bakelite plastic	formaldehyde
Barometers, broken	mercury
Baths	chloroform, trichloroethylene
Batteries	mercury, cadmium
Books, old	moulds and fungi
Brake/clutch linings	asbestos
Building structures	asbestos, formaldehyde, radon
Caravans	formaldehyde
Carbonless copy paper	formaldehyde
Carpets	formaldehyde, plastics, trichloroethylene
Carpet underlay	formaldehyde
Carpet and upholstery shampoo	ammonia, naphthalene
Carrier bags	plastics (polyethylene, low density)

Item	Chemicals
Caulking compounds	acetone, xylene
Cavity wall insulation	formaldehyde
Chewing gum	plastics
Chipboard	formaldehyde, pentachlorophenol, phenol
Chrome polish	ammonia
Cigarette smoke	aldehydes, ammonia, benzopyrenes, carbon monoxide, nitrogen dioxide
Cleaning products	ammonia, toluene
Clothing	formaldehyde
Clingfilm	PVC (polyvinyl chloride), plasticizer
Clutch/brake linings	asbestos
Coal fires	benzopyrenes, cadmium, carbon monoxide, mercury
Coffee, decaffeinated	methylene chloride, trichlorethylene
Colour sprays for leather and plastics	methylene chloride
Cookware, aluminium	aluminium
Cookware, enamel	cadmium
Correction fluid	naphthalene, plastics, 1,1,1-trichloroethane
Cosmetics	aluminium
Cosmic rays	radiation
Cushions	plastics (polyurethane)
Damp treatments	toluene
Decaffeinated coffee	methylene chloride, trichloroethylene
Decaffeinated tea	methylene chloride
Defoliant	pentachlorophenol
Degreasers	acetone, trichloroethylene
Deodorants/antiperspirants	aluminium, formaldehyde
Detergents	ammonia, benzene, formaldehyde
Dishwashers	chloroform, trichloroethane
Disinfectant	diethylene glycol, formaldehyde
Drink cans	aluminium
Dry-cleaned items	dry-cleaning fluids

Item	Chemicals
Dry-cleaning fluids	ammonia, benzene, carbon tetrachloride, naphthalene, perchloroethylene, toluene, trichloroethylene, xylene
Dyers and fixatives	formaldehyde
Egg boxes	plastics (blown polystyrene), CFCs
Enamel cookware	cadmium
Epoxy resins	plastics
Exhaust, vehicle	carbon monoxide, lead
Exposure meters, photographic	selenium oxide
Fabric finishes/treatments	formaldehyde
Fabric softeners	ammonia
Face powders and cosmetics	talcum
Fire blankets	asbestos
Flame resistant fabric	formaldehyde
Floor polish	ammonia
Flour	cadmium
Fluorescent light tubes	mercury
Foam rubber	formaldehyde, plastics (polyurethane)
Foams, polyurethane	CFCs, plastics, toluene
Food packages	plastics
Fragrances	trichloroethylene
Fungicides	borates
Furniture	formaldehyde
Furniture polish	ammonia
Gas appliances	carbon monoxide, formaldehyde, nitrogen dioxide, sulphur dioxide
Gas cookers	carbon monoxide, formaldehyde, nitrogen dioxide, sulphur dioxide
Gas waterheaters	carbon monoxide, formaldehyde, nitrogen dioxide, sulphur dioxide
Glass cleaners	ammonia, naphthalene
Glass-fibre insulation	formaldehyde
Glue	acetone, ammonia, formaldehyde, naphthalene, toluene
Golf balls (centre of)	mercury
Granite	radiation
Hair colour restorers	lead
Hair permanent chemicals	ammonia, formaldehyde

Item	Chemicals
Hair setting lotion and gels	ammonia, formaldehyde, polyvinylpyrolidone (PVP)
Hair sprays	methylene chloride, formaldehyde, plastic polyvinylpyrolidone (PVP)
Hardboard	formaldehyde
Heat pumps	CFCs
Heaters, electric storage (over 15 years old)	asbestos
Heaters, paraffin	carbon monoxide, nitrogen dioxide
Hexamine camping stove fuel	formaldehyde
High tension power lines	radiation
Household cleaning products	ammonia, formaldehyde, perchloroethylene, toluene, trichloroethylene, xylene
Household cleaning products, old	carbon tetrachloride
House plants	moulds and fungi
Inhalers, asthma	CFCs
Ink, printer's	ammonia, formaldehyde, phenol, toluene, xylene
Insecticides	benzene, borates
Insect repellants	formaldehyde
Insulation materials	formaldehyde
Ionizers, old	ozone
Ironing board covers, silver	plastics
Ironing board mats (old style)	asbestos
Kettle descaler	formic acid
Lacquers	acetone, amyl acetate, ethyl acetate
Laser printers	ozone, nitrogen dioxide
Laundry starch sprays	formaldehyde
Leather cleaners	amyl acetate
Leather colour sprays	methylene chloride
Leather/suede protection sprays	trichloroethane
Leather tanning agents	formaldehyde, methylene chloride
Light tubes, fluorescent	mercury
Luminous clock and watch dials	radiation
Matches	antimony
Masonry biocides	borates, tributyltin oxide

Item	Chemicals
Mattresses	formaldehyde, plastics (polyurethane)
MDF (medium density fibreboard) woodboard	formaldehyde
Metal polish	ammonia
Mobile homes	formaldehyde
Moss and weed killers	ammonia
Mothballs	naphthalene
Nail polish/varnish	acetone, amyl acetate, ethyl acetate, formaldehyde, xylene
Newsprint	formaldehyde
Nylon	plastics
Oven cleaners	sodium hydroxide
Oven gloves	asbestos
Paint and paintwork	ammonia, formaldehyde, lead, phenol, plastics, trichloroethylene
Paint strippers	diethylene glycol, methylene chloride
Paint thinners	chloroform, methylene chloride, toluene, xylene
Paper	formaldehyde
Paraffin heaters	carbon monoxide, nitrogen dioxide
Pens and markers	acetone, ammonia, toluene, xylene
Perfumes	aldehydes
Pesticides	('inert' ingredient) trichloroethylene
Petrol	benzene
Photocopiers	ammonia, ozone, selenium oxide
Photocopiers, old style 'wet'	ammonia
Photographic chemicals	formaldehyde
Pigments	cadmium
Pillows	polyurethane foam
Plasters and paints, textured	asbestos
Plastics	cadmium, plastics, polyethylene, toluene
Plastics burning	toluene
Plywood	formaldehyde, pentachlorophenol, phenol
Polyester	plastics
Polystyrene	CFCs, plastics

Item	Chemicals
Polyurethane foams	CFCs, plastics, toluene
Printer's ink	ammonia, formaldehyde, phenol, toluene, xylene
Refrigerant	ammonia (old refrigerators), CFCs
Satellite dishes	radiation
Shampoos	formaldehyde
Shampoos, dandruff	selenium oxide
Shoe polish liquid	methylene chloride, perchloroethylene, 1,1,1-trichloroethane, trichloroethylene, xylene
Shower curtains	plastics (polyvinyl chloride, PVC)
Showers, hot	chloroform, trichloroethylene
Silk	formaldehyde
'Silver' foil	aluminium
Simmering pads	asbestos
Slug pellets	metaldehyde, methiocarb
Smog	acrolein, aldehydes, formaldehyde, ozone
Smoke detectors	radiation
Smoke, tobacco	aldehydes, ammonia, benzopyrenes, carbon monoxide, formaldehyde, lead, radiation
Smoke, wood	aldehydes, formaldehyde
Soil stabilizers	formaldehyde
Solar cells	selenium oxide
Solder	antimony, cadmium, lead
Solvents	amyl acetate, methylene chloride, perchloroethane, 1,1,1-trichloroethane, trichloroethylene, toluene, xylene
Spray mount	1,1,1-trichloroethane
Stain removers	ammonia, benzene, diethylene glycol, naphthalene, perchloroethylene, toluene, 1,1,1-trichloroethane, trichloroethylene
Starch sprays (laundry)	formaldehyde
Stoves, woodburning	benzopyrenes
Suede/leather protection sprays	trichloroethane

Item	Chemicals
Talcum powder	talcum
Tanning agents, leather	formaldehyde, methylene chloride
Tea	aluminium
Tea, decaffeinated	methylene chloride
Teflon	plastics (polytetrafluorethylene)
Termite control, professional	chlordane
Textured plasters and paints	asbestos
Thermometers, broken	mercury
Timber, treated	borates
Tissues	formaldehyde
Toasters, old	asbestos
Tobacco smoke	aldehydes, ammonia, benzopyrenes, carbon monoxide, formaldehyde, lead, radiation
Toilet cleaners	sodium hydrogen sulphate
Toilet freshener blocks	paradichlorobenzene
Toothpaste	fluoride
Toys	polyethylene
Traffic fumes	carbon monoxide, lead
TVs, old	radiation
Varnishes	plastics (polyurethane)
Vehicle clutch and brake linings	asbestos
Veneers	formaldehyde, lindane
VDUs	radiation
Wallpaper	formaldehyde
Wallpaper cleaners	ammonia, naphthalene
Washing machines, clothes	chloroform
Water, drinking	chloroform, fluoride, lead, trichloroethylene
Waterproofing agents	formaldehyde
Water vapour	chloroform
Weed and moss killers	ammonia
Window cleaner	ammonia
Wood-boring insect control, professional	chlordane
Woodburning stoves	benzopyrenes
Wood fillers/hardeners	organic peroxide, styrene
Wood smoke	aldehydes, formaldehyde

Item	Chemicals
Wood preservatives/treatments	carbendazim, creosote, cypermethrin, dieldrin, pentachlorophenol, permethrin, tributyltin oxide (TBTO)
Wood varnishes and finishers	benzene, formaldehyde, lead, plastics (polyurethane)
Woodworm treatments	lindane, pyrethroids
X-rays	radiation

Important

If you are in any doubt about the safe disposal of any chemical product, please contact your local council for advice.

CHEMICAL DATA SHEETS

Substance	Sources	Hazards/Toxicity
ACETONE	caulking compounds degreasers glues lacquers nail polish/varnish remover pens and markers photocopiers wood hardeners	Acetone is a moderately toxic solvent if swallowed or inhaled. Skin contact can cause irritation. If inhaled in high quantities it may lead to drowsiness.
ALDEHYDES	perfumes preservatives smog (acetaldehyde and acrolein) tobacco smoke wood smoke	Exposure to aldehydes may cause headaches, irritation to eyes and mucous membranes, drowsiness and fatigue. Aldehydes can pass easily through the blood−brain barrier and may induce changes in short-term memory and provoke anxiety. They are suspected carcinogens and are known to cause free radical damage to cells (see Chapter 7).
ALLETHRIN see PYRETHROIDS		
ALPHACYPERMETHRIN see PYRETHROIDS		

ALUMINIUM	air pollution
	aluminium cookware
	aluminium (or 'silver')
	   foil
	antacids
	antiperspirant/
	   deodorants
	baking powder
	base of some false teeth
		Aluminium can be absorbed through the skin, lungs and digestive system. In some people it may cause a contact dermatitis.
		   Substantial ingestion or exposure to aluminium may precipitate colic,

IMPORTANT NOTE: Many of the symptoms listed under the Hazards/Toxicity sections are also symptoms of specific illnesses. If symptoms are persistent, a doctor should be consulted before concluding that they are chemically induced.

Protection	Impact on Environment/Wildlife
If products containing acetone are used indoors the area must be well ventilated. Acetone is flammable.	No data found.
Vitamin C, B$_1$ and L-cysteine together with B$_6$ for assimilation provide very powerful protection against aldehydes and also provide protection for smokers. Beta carotene, the substance found in yellow and orange vegetables and yellow/orange fruit, protects the lungs from damage from inhaled pollutants, including those in tobacco smoke. See Chapter 7 for more details.	No data found.
The body's natural calcium and phosphorus balance prevents aluminium from accumulating in the body and brain. Adequate magnesium is also important. An abnormally low zinc intake may allow aluminium to accumulate in the brain. Aluminium interferes with all these minerals and iron, and a deficiency allows more	Aluminium is leached out of the soil in rivers and lakes by acid rain; this affects the aquatic environment by killing fish and birds which feed on water insects.

Substance	Sources	Hazards/Toxity
ALUMINIUM (continued)	drink cans drinking water in peaty/ soft water areas food additives: E173, E554, E556, E541 slug killer some soy-based baby formulas tea toothpaste tubes (not plastic variety)	memory loss, nervousness, irritation, constipation, loss of appetite, nausea, skin ailments, twitching of leg muscles, excessive perspiration, loss of energy, numbness, liver and kidney disorders. Long-term, low-level aluminium exposure has a link with the development of Alzheimer's disease (senile dementia).
AMMONIA	carpet and upholstery shampoos cigarette smoke chrome polishes detergents disinfectants dry-cleaning fluids fabric softeners furniture and floor polish glass cleaners glues hair permanent chemicals hair setting gels	Can cause burns; fumes are irritant to the respiratory system and eyes. If used in a confined space, especially a warm atmosphere without sufficient ventilation, the fumes can be hazardous. The ammonia solution is poisonous. Ammonium thioglycollate in hair perm solutions can cause contact dermatitis and is a strong allergen.

Protection	Impact on Environment/Wildlife

aluminium to be absorbed. It is common for people who are anaemic to have raised aluminium levels.

In order to protect the body, minerals should be supplied adequately in the diet and absorbed well in the digestive system. The kidneys must also be functioning well.

In addition to avoiding the main sources of aluminium, be aware that it is also present in salt to stop it caking, as part of the bleaching process of white flour, as an emulsifier in processed cheese, in the manufacture of pickles and as a compound base for some chewing gum. An alternative to baking powder is baking soda which doesn't contain aluminium, or you can make your own baking powder by mixing 1 part baking soda with 2 parts cream of tartar and 2 parts arrowroot powder.

Low birth weight or premature babies or those with kidney weakness should not be given highly processed soy-based formulas as soy beans are naturally high in aluminium and the child may be zinc, iron and calcium deficient. Stainless steel cookware is a safe alternative to aluminium, but avoid enamel, especially if it is old, cracked or red-orange. It can be a source of **cadmium.**

If you do use cleaners or disinfectants which contain ammonia, make sure that there is adequate ventilation and leave the room until the vapours have dispersed. For safer alternatives see the end of this chapter and Chapter 8.

If you have clothing dry-cleaned, hang it in the fresh air for at least one to two days, or at least keep it out of your bedroom until it has had a chance to evaporate — hang in a wardrobe *only* when thoroughly aired, especially during the winter when the windows are likely to be closed. Allow

Ammonia and products containing it are a threat to aquatic life and adversely affect terrestrial environments. Avoid using or buying ammonia whenever possible. Ammonia appears on the EC List II 'Grey List' of substances which require environmental quality standards and should not be at such a level that it could threaten freshwater fish.

Substance	Sources	Hazards/Toxity
AMMONIA (continued)	metal polish paints pens and markers photocopiers (old style 'wet' type) printer's ink refrigerant in some old refrigerators stain removers wallpaper cleaners weed and moss killers window and some floor cleaners	
AMYL ACETATE	lacquers nail varnish solvent mixtures	Amyl acetate is a solvent which is moderately toxic if inhaled or swallowed. Breathing high concentrations for a prolonged period can induce eye, nose, and throat irritation, fatigue, headache and drowsiness. Products containing this chemical are highly flammable.
ANTIMONY	matches solder	Antimony and its compounds are highly toxic if inhaled or swallowed and can cause skin irritation.

Protection	Impact on Environment/Wildlife
continental quilts to air for at least two days before using them – down and other fillings tend to 'hold' volatile chemicals in large quantities. Keep the windows open in the car when taking dry-cleaned items home.	
Never mix household products which contain ammonia with bleach or products which contain bleach. The mixture will result in the release of hazardous fumes (for more details see Chart 3.3 in Chapter 3).	
If you have your hair permed several times a year ensure that you follow the nutritional suggestions outlined on page 168 and in Chapter 7. Begin about three days before the perm and continue for at least a week after to enable the body to detoxify.	
The mineral magnesium helps the body to eliminate ammonia via the urine. Good sources of magnesium include fresh fruit and vegetables, especially black grapes and raisins, nuts and seeds, soya flour, whole grains and brewer's yeast. The amino acids asparagine, aspartic acid and glutamic acid also detoxify ammonia.	
Use products containing this chemical only in well ventilated areas and keep it away from flames and sparks.	Many chemicals have the potential to pollute water environments and solvents are used in a wide range of household and DIY products, most of which are disposed of down the drain. Wherever an alternative exists it is advisable to use a product which biodegrades harmlessly. See Chapter 8 for more information.
Avoid breathing the fumes from burning matches or when soldering.	No data found.

Substance	Sources	Hazards/Toxity

ASBESTOS	asbestos* insulation blocks and building materials
	moulded asbestos coverings for water tanks
	some cement products
	some cushion floorings
	electric storage heaters installed before 1976
	fire blankets
	fire proofing of steel girders sprayed on the building site
	fire protection and heat insulation boards up until 1980
	flue pipes
	garage/shed roofs
	guttering
	old heat-proof mats
	old ironing board mats
	old lagging around pipes and boilers
	particulates in the air around high traffic areas
	some oven gloves
	some plastic tiles
	rain water pipes
	some roofing felts
	some simmering pads
	textured plasters and paints
	old toasters
	vehicle brake and clutch linings
		Asbestos particles are suspended in the air in urban areas and wherever asbestos in older building materials and appliances is beginning to disintegrate. Inhaled asbestos particles do not degrade in the lungs and may lead to the gradual development of lung cancer or mesothelioma, a cancer of the chest wall.
		    Smokers who either work with or are exposed to asbestos are 90 times more vulnerable to the development of lung cancer than non-smokers.
		    There are three types of asbestos: blue (which is considered the most harmful), brown, and white, which accounts for 95 percent of all asbestos used.
		    All urban dwellers have asbestos in their lung tissue. The Environmental Protection Agency (EPA) states that there is no safe level of exposure to asbestos and has included it in the list of 'priority pollutants' classified as hazardous to human health.

BENDIOCARB	insecticide	Bendiocarb is present in a number of household aerosol pesticide products. It is an anticholinesterase agent which is highly toxic if swallowed. It can be hazardous to children and

* Since 1986 all European products containing asbestos have carried a warning label.

Protection	Impact on Environment/Wildlife
Asbestos is actually a naturally occurring mineral made up of small fibres. It presents a problem only when the dust becomes airborne; this may happen when it gets old and cracked or if sanded, drilled or dismantled.	The data on asbestos particles in ground, surface and drinking water is restricted. Its impact on the environment is limited to its effect on living entities.

Asbestos must be removed by an expert. If you suspect that there may be a dangerous source of asbestos in a building where you work, live, or study it is important that you contact your local environmental health department.

If you find asbestos and need help or advice contact The Asbestos Information Centre, St Andrews House, Epsom, Surrey, KT19 8AH, Telephone (03727) 42055.

Vitamin A, especially beta carotene, has been shown in research to provide a certain amount of protection against cell mutation and the development of lung cancer.

There are numerous natural solutions to ant infestation and cockroaches (see the end of this chapter); if wasps are an overwhelming problem the chemical should be used with care. As with all aerosols, tiny droplets of chemicals are released into the air and are easily	Bendiocarb is toxic to bees and is dangerous to fish, birds and wildlife.

Substance	Sources	Hazards/Toxity
BENDIOCARB (continued)		pets if not used according to the directions.
BENZENE	cigarette smoke detergents some DIY or household products dry-cleaning fluids glues insecticides lead substitute in unleaded petrol paints petrol petroleum mixtures resins rubber stain removers wood varnishes/finishes	Benzene is a chronic poison derived from petroleum. Small repeated exposure through inhaling benzene vapours can cause dizziness, fatigue, headache, pallor, lightheadedness, disorientation and loss of appetite. It is toxic, carcinogenic and teratogenic and may cause chromosome changes in human reproductive cells. It can be absorbed through the skin and is a skin irritant. Benzene exposure can also lead to aplastic anaemia and leukaemia in extreme cases. Benzene is included in the Environmental Protection Agency list of 'priority pollutants' classified as hazardous to human health. It is also highly flammable.
BENZOPYRENES	coal fires factory emissions tobacco smoke woodburning stoves	Benzopyrenes are suspected carcinogenic agents.

Protection	Impact on Environment/Wildlife
inhaled, so wear a mask and leave the area as soon as possible. Protect the skin and eyes. The spray should not be used in a confined, unventilated area.	
Avoid breathing in petrol fumes, even when you fill your car, and use any household and DIY products which contain benzene with very good ventilation. Better still, choose products which are free of this chemical. Benzene is an aromatic solvent of which phenol is an alcohol derivative. Vitamin C helps to protect the body against pollutants and is helpful in detoxifying the body after exposure to petrol fumes.	No data found, but all solvents should be used only when absolutely necessary; because of their widespread use their disposal may pose environmental problems.

Have chimneys swept regularly and if you use woodburning stoves ensure that the chimney is efficient and that no smoke is escaping into the room.
   Antioxidant vitamins and minerals are important in protecting the cells and helping the body to cope with free radical damage and detoxify pollutants – a good multiple vitamin/mineral formula which supplies A, C, E, selenium, zinc, magnesium and calcium is an important addition to the diet if you live in an industrial area or use a fire in a badly ventilated room.
   Vitamin C is a specific anticarcinogen against benzo(a)pyrene.
	No data found.

Substance	Sources	Hazards/Toxity
BIOALLETHRIN see PYRETHROIDS		
BIORESMETHRIN see PYRETHROIDS		
BORATES	ant powders fungicides household garden, timber and masonry treatments insecticides (Various derivatives of boric acid, including disodium octaborate (borax), are used in all these products, not the acid itself.)	Boric acid can be moderately toxic if it is swallowed, may be an eye irritant and can cause death in large doses.
CADMIUM	batteries (rechargeable) coal burning old galvanized items industrial contamination in the air low-zinc refined foods such as white flour paints* pigment in plastics (bright yellow/red) red or orange enamelled cookware tobacco smoke zinc smelting *Cadmium is now added instead of lead additives.	Cadmium is a heavy metal which causes free radical damage to cells. It can accumulate in the kidneys and arteries causing high blood pressure, arteriosclerosis, retention of sodium and kidney damage. High exposure can also result in hair loss, osteoporosis, sore joints and dry scaly skin. In children cadmium can cause bone abnormality due to disturbed calcium metabolism. Cadmium poisoning is associated with bronchitis, anaemia, gastro-intestinal symptoms and cancer. It is stored in the liver and kidneys, and the total body concentration increases with age.
CARBENDAZIM	biocides fungicides wood treatments	Moderately hazardous with skin contact.

Protection	Impact on Environment/Wildlife
Keep boric acid well away from children — 5–10 grams can cause death if ingested. Excessive exposure to boric acid compounds may lead to reduced fertility.	Borate pesticides are considered safe for use in roofs inhabited by bats.
The mineral selenium helps the body to rid itself of toxic cadmium. Its antioxidant effects act with vitamin C to protect the body against free radical damage to cells. For more details about free radicals see Chapter 7. Zinc in adequate quantities can reverse cadmium poisoning and keep its toxic effects under control. Cadmium has many structural similarities to zinc, and when zinc intake is low the body will store cadmium instead. If daily zinc intake is adequate or high, zinc is stored and cadmium is excreted. In iron deficiency (particularly anaemia) cadmium is more easily absorbed into the body; in turn, exposure to high levels of cadmium (cadmium poisoning) can deplete the body's iron. Dispose of old red or orange enamelled cookware, especially if it is chipped. See Chapter 10 for details of plasticware which does not contain cadmium.	Cadmium and its compounds are listed in the Government 'Red List' and the EC List I 'Black List' of chemicals considered to be so toxic, persistent or bio-accumulative in the environment that steps should be taken to eliminate pollution by them.
Protect skin and eyes and ensure there is adequate ventilation when using this chemical. Keep pets and children away from the treated area.	Carbendazim is harmful to fish and is moderately soil persistent.

Substance	Sources	Hazards/Toxity
CARBON MONOXIDE	cigarette smoke coal fires/boilers incomplete combustion of fuel improperly installed or serviced gas cookers/ appliances/ waterheaters* photocopiers vehicle exhaust	Carbon monoxide is odourless and tasteless so it is difficult to detect. It is dangerous because it causes oxygen deprivation by combining with haemoglobin (in the blood), 'poisoning' the red blood cells and preventing them from carrying oxygen around the body. The brain and heart principally require a constant, high oxygen supply and are the organs primarily affected by decreased oxygen supply. Decreased stamina and impaired coordination are common symptoms of carbon monoxide build-up in the blood. Symptoms of chronic low-level exposure to carbon monoxide in the early stages include non-specific symptoms such as headache, tightness across the forehead, confusion, nausea, vomiting, abdominal pain, fatigue, dizziness, and chest pains. The effect that carbon monoxide has on the mental faculties is what makes it so dangerous, even in the early stages — victims are often unable to recognize what is happening to them. Because these symptoms

*When appliances are functioning correctly, gas is a perfectly safe fuel. Any danger comes from partially burned gas escaping from appliances which may build up in a badly ventilated room.

Protection	Impact on Environment/Wildlife
Have all gas appliances, fireplaces etc., checked and cleaned regularly by an approved service – they should be registered with the Confederation for the Registration of Gas Installers (CORGI).	Carbon monoxide is indirectly one of the 'greenhouse' gases: it reacts with chemicals which would normally remove methane and oxidizes to carbon dioxide, which contributes to global warming.

Watch out for badly fitted pipes, cracks and discoloured paint. Ensure that the maintenance engineer checks chimneys and flues for blockages.

Only buy appliances that conform to British safety standards and be very very wary of second-hand appliances.

Ensure that there is adequate ventilation when using gas appliances or fireplaces.

A study published in the *Journal of the Air Pollution Control Association* showed that even well maintained gas cookers emitted relatively high levels of carbon monoxide. Placing pans over burners decreases the airflow and causes a reduction in the combustion of the gas flame, thus producing higher levels of carbon monoxide.

Carbon monoxide circulates throughout the home and, depending upon the level of ventilation, may remain in the air for several hours. Using a number of burners at the same time, or leaving a pan simmering, can result in levels which pose a risk to health.

If you are pregnant, avoid situations where you are likely to be exposed to carbon monoxide as it can retard foetal growth if inhaled at very high concentrations.

Substance	Sources	Hazards/Toxity
CARBON MONOXIDE (continued)		could be mistaken for flu or even food poisoning, it is important to look for clues such as similar symptoms among other members of the household and the recurrence of these symptoms at specific times or in particular places.

Carbon monoxide poisoning causes an average of over 1000 deaths a year in Britain. It accounts for one third of all deaths by poisoning and is the main cause of such deaths in children. Carbon monoxide is toxic to red blood cells, and if the exposure is severe, convulsions, coma, brain damage or death may occur.

If you suspect carbon monoxide poisoning, move the victim into the fresh air *immediately* – if there is no breathing perform mouth to mouth resuscitation. **There is no danger of carbon monoxide poisoning to the resuscitator.** Ask someone to call an ambulance immediately as oxygen will be needed.

The American Heart Association reported in the late 1980s on a condition called 'urban angina syndrome'. This has similar physical manifestations to angina pectoris, a symptom of ischaemia, which occurs when the heart muscle fails to get adequate oxygen to function properly. It can occur when a person is

Protection	Impact on Environment/Wildlife

Substance	Sources	Hazards/Toxity
CARBON MONOXIDE (continued)		emotionally excited or during physical exertion. Scientists describing the urban angina syndrome have identified carbon monoxide as its source. They are warning people with heart disease to be cautious if exercising in a badly polluted area, because their exposure to carbon monoxide could lead to pain or serious illness. Investigators at three major American medical centres found that even low-level exposure to carbon monoxide during exercise increases the chance of heart patients experiencing the pains associated with angina pectoris. The possibility of fatalities from carbon monoxide poisoning are more likely in houses with sealed windows and open-flue coal appliances. High winds have resulted in carbon monoxide poisoning because the wind can induce greater suction back into the house via a 'safety' vent on one side of the house.
CARBON TETRACHLORIDE	old DIY and household products (not used in current products) dry-cleaning fluids many industrial processes	CTC is a chlorinated solvent which is poisonous if swallowed or inhaled or absorbed through the skin. It is a liver toxicant, an irritant and cancer trigger, and excessive exposure may cause damage to the optic and cranial nerves as well as liver and kidney damage.

Protection	Impact on Environment/Wildlife
If you have clothing dry-cleaned, hang it in the fresh air for at least one to two days, or at least keep it out of your bedroom until it has had a chance to evaporate – hang it in a wardrobe only when thoroughly aired, especially during the winter when the windows are likely to be closed. Leave car windows open when transporting clothing and other dry-cleaned items home. Allow continental quilts to air for at least two days before using them,	Carbon tetrachloride is one of the 129 substances on the EC List I 'Black List' of chemicals considered to be so toxic, persistent or bio-accumulative in the environment that steps should be taken to eliminate pollution by them.

Substance	Sources	Hazards/Toxity
CARBON TETRACHLORIDE (continued)		
CHLORDANE	wood treatments	This chemical is illegal for amateur use in the UK, therefore exposure to it is likely to come only from property treated by a professional pest control company. Chlordane has been used since 1948 as a pesticide in the USA and for a number of years in the UK. By 1983 the US Environmental Protection Agency had banned its use except for professional termite control. Chlordane is included in the USEPA list of 'priority pollutants' classified as hazardous to human health. Like DDT, it accumulates in the fatty tissues of the body, especially in the digestive tract, and it may take many years before its toxicity is manifested. Its ban was based on evidence that it causes cancer in certain laboratory animals and is persistent in the environment. Acute exposure to chlordane may cause irritability or dizziness.
CHLOROFLUORO CARBONS (CFCs)	aerosol propellant air conditioners asthma inhalers	Chlorinated fluorocarbons are inert gases comprising chlorine, fluorine and

Protection	Impact on Environment/Wildlife
as down and other fillings tend to 'hold the chemicals in large quantities. Contact your local environmental health department for information on how to dispose of old DIY and household items which contain CTC. Use only current DIY and household products.	
If you have any old household products containing chlordane contact your local town hall (Environmental Health Department) or Friends of the Earth for advice on its safe disposal.	Chlordane's effects can continue for at least 5 years – the 1982 National Research Council Report estimated up to 20 years – and it persists in both soil and water. It is highly toxic to fish and other water organisms, bees, birds and livestock. Never dispose of old garden chemicals containing chlordane into sinks, toilets, drains, rivers etc., as wildlife, fish and drinking water supplies are all vulnerable to this hazardous chemical.
If everyone decided never to buy an aerosol again, manufacturers would put their products into pump-action	CFCs are extremely stable airborne compounds that are not destroyed before reaching the stratosphere. Up

Substance	Sources	Hazards/Toxity
CHLOROFLUORO CARBONS (CFCs) (continued)	heat pumps insulation materials 'foamed' or 'blown' polystyrene refrigerators safety gear urethane foams	carbon and are not considered toxic. It is their destruction of the earth's protective ozone layer that makes them a threat to our health. As the ozone layer is depleted, more harmful ultraviolet rays from the sun reach the earth. Researchers estimate that with increased exposure to ultraviolet rays there will be a sharp rise in the number of skin cancers and eye diseases like cataracts – this is due to UV forming free radicals; see Chapter 7 for more information on free radicals.
CHLOROFORM	vapour from: baths dishwashers hot showers washing machines paint thinners and strippers propellants refrigerants the bonding of certain plastics using chloroform	Acute exposure can cause drowsiness or depression as chloroform has anaesthetic effects. Chronic exposure to chloroform vapour may ultimately affect the liver and kidneys. It used to be used as an anaesthetic.
CREOSOTE	wood preserver	Creosote contains **phenols** and is carcinogenic. It is extremely poisonous if inhaled or swallowed or absorbed through the skin.
CYPERMETHRIN	insecticide wood preservative	Cypermethrin may cause mild skin and eye irritation in mammals and it may be a skin sensitizer. Toxic exposure may cause temporary tingling and

Protection	Impact on Environment/Wildlife
sprays which are just as effective and far less wasteful and dangerous. Although the use of CFCs in aerosols is declining, the other propellants being used, for example butane, are extremely dangerous as they are highly flammable. If you wish to dispose of a refrigerator contact the retailers to see whether when you buy a new fridge they will take the old one away and safely recycle the CFCs. Another option is to sell the fridge on or donate it to a local charity. Buy pump-action sprays where possible and keep all aerosol products away from children. Vitamins A, C and E with the mineral selenium protect the body against free radical damage; for detailed information see Chapter 7.	there, high-energy UV splits CFCs releasing an atom of chlorine. This sets up a chain reaction which destroys ozone molecules. Scientists have estimated that if the holes in the ozone layer continue to grow, phytoplankton in the oceans will die which will cause severe changes in the oceans' ecosystems. Halon, a chemical used in fire extinguishers, is also a threat to the earth's ozone layer and it has a synergistic effect with CFCs, intensifying its damaging effects. CFCs also contribute to the greenhouse effect – see the glossary for more information.
Ensure that there is adequate ventilation in any room where the water vapour will be released. Close bathroom or kitchen doors to prevent the vapour from entering the air in the rest of the home, and open a window. Deficiencies in certain vitamins and minerals may leave you more vulnerable to the negative effects of air pollution. For more information on how to protect the body see Chapter 7.	No data found.
Wear protective clothing and protect the eyes. Keep children and animals away until dry. Preferably do not use creosote on indoor timbers as its toxic vapours can remain in indoor air for several weeks.	Creosote is toxic to fish, and dangerous to animals while still wet.
Take precautions not to breathe spray mist and wear protective clothing, including eye protection. Wash skin immediately if the chemical comes into contact with it. Avoid contaminating food.	Cypermethrin is extremely dangerous to fish and bees.

Substance	Sources	Hazards/Toxity
CYPERMETHRIN (continued)		numbness of exposed areas, especially the face, and lung irritation.
DELTAMETHRIN see PYRETHROIDS		
DICHLOROMETHANE see METHYLENE CHLORIDE		
DICHLORVOS	flea collars fly killer blocks and other products insecticide spray	Poisonous through all routes of ingestion — swallowing, inhaling, absorption through skin — and is a possible carcinogen. Dichlorvos is an anticholinesterase agent (see glossary).
DIELDRIN	insecticide seed dressings sheep dips and sprays wood preservative	Dieldrin is soluble in fat but not water and is therefore stored in fat deposits in the body from where it may be released into the bloodstream during crash diets or rapid weight loss. Dieldrin is 40 times more toxic than DDT when absorbed through the skin. It was used as a timber treatment in buildings until its health hazards became apparent and has been banned in Britain since 1988.
DIETHYLENE GLYCOL	antifreeze some disinfectant products paint strippers some stain removers	If inhaled, diethylene glycol can be highly toxic and has an irritant effect on the skin.

Protection	Impact on Environment/Wildlife
Avoid using these products in badly ventilated areas and keep them away from rooms occupied by the very young, sick or elderly, and the kitchen where food is prepared. See the end of this chapter for alternative suggestions.	Dichlorvos is toxic to bees and fish and is included in the Government 'Red List' of substances to be subject to stricter controls for both direct and indirect discharges to water, and on the EC List I 'Black List' of substances considered to be so toxic, persistent or bio-accumulative in the environment that steps should be taken to eliminate pollution by them.
If you still have any products containing this chemical, contact your local environmental health department or Friends of the Earth (see Chapter 8) for advice on safe disposal. **It is unsafe to use this chemical.**	Dieldrin is extremely persistent in the environment and concentrates in the food chain. It is particularly toxic to quails and other birds and to the mammals which feed on them. It has been banned for use by farmers for over a decade but still contaminates rivers — it is persistent in the soil for years. It appears on the Government 'Red List' and the EC List I 'Black List' of chemicals considered to be so toxic, persistent or bio-accumulative in the environment that steps should be taken to eliminate pollution by them.
Use only in a well ventilated area and keep away from the skin and eyes.	No data found.

Substance	Sources	Hazards/Toxity
DIETHYL TOLUAMIDE (DEET)	household insect repellants	Deet is poisonous, particularly if absorbed through the skin or swallowed. It has caused deaths. Repeated exposure even to dilute solutions has been known to affect the central nervous system.
DIQUAT	general weedkiller	Prolonged use and exposure has been known to induce cataracts, and gastrointestinal disturbances such as vomiting and diarrhoea have occurred. It is rare, but diquat has also been linked with pulmonary fibrosis. Diquat may be fatal if swallowed or absorbed through the skin and also if inhaled; there is no known antidote. In animal tests it was linked with foetal damage and reduced fertility.
ETHYL ACETATE	lacquers nail varnish	This solvent has a highly irritant vapour and is moderately toxic if swallowed, inhaled or absorbed through the skin. Repeated exposure may cause damage to the eyes.
FLUORIDE	dental treatments some drinking water supplies fluoride toothpastes produce grown with chemical fertilizers smoke from steelworks tea	Studies by United States Government toxicologists reveal that fluoride in high doses can harm bones and teeth and cause cancer. Excessive doses can also reduce blood vitamin C levels, cause birth defects, genetic damage and

Protection	Impact on Environment/Wildlife
Protect skin and eyes and keep away from children. If used in a hot atmosphere the rate of absorption through the skin is intensified. If this chemical is used it should only be when absolutely necessary and never for protracted periods.	No data found.
If you must use diquat, keep it away from children and avoid contact with eyes and skin. It is harmful to animals and they should be kept well clear of the treated area for at least a full day. There is disagreement as to the actual time-lapse before diquat-treated food crops are safe to eat. It is best to err on the side of safety and keep this chemical well clear of anything you intend to consume. If you do use garden chemicals, vitamin C can help your body to detoxify the small amounts which may be ingested or inhaled. 250 mg taken before the work and another 250 mg taken after is generally a safe dose; see Chapter 7 for contraindications to taking vitamin C.	Diquat's toxicity to fish is low. In the environment, diquat is very persistent and does not break down. It can contaminate water and in high concentrations causes the loss of potassium and phosphate from the soil.
Use only in a well ventilated area.	No data found.
Using fluoride toothpastes merely increases exposure to this toxic chemical — the alleged beneficial effects of fluoridating our water supplies have never been proven. A child who regularly swallows fluoridated toothpaste may ingest far more than the estimated 'safe' dose of fluoride.	Fluoride is an industrial waste chemical produced by the steel and aluminium industry. It was considered to be a poison until the 1930s when the industry started to have a problem with its disposal. Now it is sold to water companies who add it to domestic supplies in certain areas of Great Britain.

Substance	Sources	Hazards/Toxity
FLUORIDE (continued)		weaken the immune system. In sensitive people fluoridated water may cause numerous symptoms from digestive and stomach disorders to hair loss, mouth ulcers, brittle nails and pricking sensations in the muscles.
		The symptoms of toxic fluoride intake can include spasmodic abdominal pain, diarrhoea, cyanosis (reduced haemoglobin in the blood), severe weakness and eventually coma.
		Fluoride inhibits enzymes including those involved in the transmission of nerve impulses. It can also interfere with body functions controlled by calcium — its strong affinity for this mineral can result in hypocalcaemia, abnormally low blood calcium, and this affects the heartbeat.
FORMALDEHYDE	adhesives bakelite plastic burning of gas/wood/oil carbon-free copy paper carpets — in the mothproofing carpet underlay chipboard and MDF board deodorants/ antiperspirants disinfectants (hospital and catering) dyes fabric treatments (easy care, non-iron)	Small quantities of formaldehyde are released into the air as it breaks down into a toxic gas. Because so many of the items we live with contain this chemical, the levels may build up in a badly ventilated, heated room. Formaldehyde is a potent irritant to the mucous membranes. In chronic exposure it can cause depression, headaches, dizziness and loss of sleep. It may also

Protection	Impact on Environment/Wildlife
Cutting down the consumption of sugar protects the teeth, and eating plenty of raw vegetables and fruit, especially carrots, strengthens the gums and teeth. Vitamin B_6 has a retarding effect on mouth lactic acid which is the cause of erosion and cavities, and vitamin B complex is preventative against fluoride toxicity. Children whose diets contain plenty of calcium and magnesium grow up with stronger and more cavity-resistant teeth.	
If your water is fluoridated, increase your consumption of vitamins B and C as blood levels of these are reduced by fluoride. The same is true for calcium and magnesium, zinc and iron. See Chapter 7 for more information on these vitamins and their food sources.	
If you think you are sensitive to formaldehyde, avoid excessive exposure to it and ensure that there is adequate ventilation in any room where the levels are likely to be high. If possible avoid buying chipboard, MDF and plywood and furniture made from these items, or seal them with a natural varnish or paint (see Chapter 8 for more details) to prevent the release of formaldehyde gas. (See Chapter 8 for the Friends of the Earth *Good Wood Guide*.)	Formaldehyde is carcinogenic to animals at 6 parts per million. It also causes mutagenic activity in a variety of microorganisms and insects.
Flame retardant nightwear is treated with a melamine formaldehyde compound. This often leaves 'free'	

Substance	Sources	Hazards/Toxity
FORMALDEHYDE (continued)	flame resistant fabrics foam rubbers gas appliances glass-fibre insulation glues hair sprays hair setting gels hardboard hexamine camping stove fuel insect repellants kerosenes laundry starch leather tanning agents mobile homes nail varnish/polish newsprint nitrogen fertilizers paints/paint strippers paper products including grocery bags photographic chemicals/paper plywood polluted air/smog printer's ink some shampoos silk soil sterilizer wet-strength tissues/paper towels tobacco smoke urea formaldehyde cavity wall insulation veneers wallpaper waterproofing agents waxed paper wood varnishes/finishes Fabrics treated with THPC release formaldehyde when wet.	act as a trigger for asthma and hypersensitivity to other irritants. It has been linked to an increased risk of cancer as it has been known to cause mutations in genetic material. In sensitive or sensitized individuals formaldehyde may produce any of the following symptoms if inhaled, or if it comes into contact with the skin: asthma burning eyes* chest pain depression diarrhoea drowsiness and dizziness dry cough/sore throat eye, throat and nose irritation* headaches* heart palpitations irritability lethargy and weakness lost or decreased sense of taste/smell nasal congestion nausea respiratory tract irritation skin rashes/itching shortness of breath sleep loss Harvard University medical research revealed that constant exposure to formaldehyde even in concentrations of less than

*Even moderate exposure to formaldehyde gas may bring on these symptoms in some people.

Protection	Impact on Environment/Wildlife
formaldehyde and possibly other chemical residues on the fabric which results in skin irritations, especially in young children. Nightwear which is untreated carries a fire warning.	

formaldehyde and possibly other chemical residues on the fabric which results in skin irritations, especially in young children. Nightwear which is untreated carries a fire warning.

In the home, levels may build up in badly ventilated rooms, and for people who suffer from respiratory complaints such as asthma or bronchitis, angina or sensitivity to petrochemicals (especially the elderly), this can be a serious threat to health. Evidence is increasing which shows that even low concentrations of combustion chemicals affect health, even though the effects are subtle and sometimes difficult to associate with exposure. By-products of gas appliances also include **formaldehyde,** various oxides, **carbon monoxide** and hydrogen cyanide.

If you own a camping stove which burns hexamine it should only be used in the open air. When burned or heated, hexamine releases formaldehyde.

Spider plants absorb formaldehyde from the air; for more information about plants and air quality see Chapter 3.

Ensure that you have enough vitamin C in your diet because it helps the body to detoxify chemicals. See Chapter 7 for more details on dietary help and detoxification.

Substance	Sources	Hazards/Toxicity
FORMALDEHYDE (continued)	Cotton items labelled as 'Mercerized' or 'Sanforized' have not been processed with formaldehyde. (For more information see *cotton* in the glossary.) Formaldehyde may be used in cosmetics to reduce bacteria count, and as a preservative, but this is uncommon due to its overpowering smell.	1 part per million could cause nervous system defects and severe memory loss in adults. In 1980 the US Chemical Institute established that inhaling formaldehyde fumes can induce cancer in rats. Because the research did not extend to human subjects and is only a suspected carcinogen in humans, no action has been taken to ban formaldehyde, or even to limit its use. Chipboard containing formaldehyde has been banned from use in public buildings in West Germany. The National Academy of Sciences in the USA has estimated that 10 to 20 percent of the general population may be susceptible to the irritant properties of formaldehyde even at extremely low concentrations. If swallowed, formaldehyde is poisonous.
FORMIC ACID	dyes fumigants insecticides kettle descalers papers refrigerants textiles	Formic acid is a highly corrosive chemical which should always be kept away from the skin and eyes. It is toxic if swallowed and produces an irritating vapour.
HCH **see LINDANE**		

Protection	Impact on Environment/Wildlife
Diluted vinegar has a descaling effect without releasing any dangerous vapours; see the end of this chapter. If you filter your water before drinking it, your kettle will naturally descale itself over a period of several weeks. Additionally, use a stainless steel descaling ball in the kettle. Other kettle descalers may contain sulphamic acid. This is also a corrosive chemical which is a skin and eye irritant and is toxic when swallowed.	No data found.

Substance	Sources	Hazards/Toxity
LEAD	air pollution from traffic exhaust caulking compounds some ceramic glazes dust carrying lead from traffic exhaust certain men's hair colour restorers lead from old paint news and magazine print, especially red areas solder tobacco smoke vegetables grown or displayed close to heavy traffic pre-war water pipes in soft water areas wood varnishes/finishes	Lead is non-biodegradable. Excessive or regular exposure allows it to accumulate in the body; it is stored largely in the bones where it can be released into tissue as the skeleton shrinks later in life. This is thought to be a significant factor in the aging process. A developing foetus and children under seven are extremely vulnerable as their nervous systems are still developing — young children absorb a greater percentage of ingested lead than older children or adults. In the first year of life the brain is still developing and the presence of lead can decrease its ultimate capacity. Damage from exposure to lead is largely irreversible and for this reason women who are pregnant should avoid exposure to lead as much as possible. For more information, and for details of how to purchase their booklet, *Guidelines for Future Parents*, contact: Foresight, Association for Preconceptual Care, The Old Vicarage, Church Lane, Witley, Godalming, Surrey, GU8 5PN. Lead from dust passes through the skin into the bloodstream; the toxic compound used in leaded petrol (tetraethyl lead) is absorbed very easily. The human body can only tolerate 1-2 mg of lead

Protection	Impact on Environment/Wildlife
Lead used to be a major constituent of paint as a drying agent, colour or corrosion preventative. Emulsion paint does not contain lead and after 1986 it was severely restricted in other paints. **Cadmium** is now used as a lead substitute.	Lead in the environment can be taken up by plants, but ultimately the impact of this heavy metal falls on us rather than the environment. Animals eating crops contaminated with lead will absorb a certain amount, but no data was found on the repercussions of ingested lead on the health of either wildlife or livestock.

Lead used to be a major constituent of paint as a drying agent, colour or corrosion preventative. Emulsion paint does not contain lead and after 1986 it was severely restricted in other paints. **Cadmium** is now used as a lead substitute.

When rubbing down old paintwork, wear a mask and protect children and pets from exposure, and clear up as quickly as possible with a wet cloth to avoid precipitating any lead dust into the air. Never clean leaded windows with a dry cloth or brush as this will cause lead dust to be released; use a mild liquid cleanser and wash your hands and the cloth thoroughly afterwards – preferably, wear rubber gloves when cleaning lead items. If old paintwork has been rubbed down in a kitchen ensure that food is stored away and all kitchen surfaces are cleaned before food is prepared. Particles of lead may be carried in the air and contaminate food and any surfaces where it is prepared.

Prevent children from picking lead from leaded windows by covering the lead strip with a clear varnish – see Chapter 8 for natural DIY products.

Water from the hot tap may have lead dissolved in it, especially in an area with soft water. If you live in a prewar house your waterpipes are likely to be made from lead. Overnight water sits in pipes and in the morning it may contain lead. It is best to let it run before drinking it. For information on *water filters* see Chapter 8. Grants are available to help you convert lead pipes to plastic ones, and some local authorities will check your tap water's lead content without charge.

If you burn wood which has been painted, and then spread the ashes in your vegetable garden, traces of lead will find their way into next year's crop. Even new gloss paints contain a trace of lead. Locate your vegetable

Lead in the environment can be taken up by plants, but ultimately the impact of this heavy metal falls on us rather than the environment. Animals eating crops contaminated with lead will absorb a certain amount, but no data was found on the repercussions of ingested lead on the health of either wildlife or livestock.

Lead is found in acidified lakes, and nematodes ingesting lead-contaminated bacteria and fungi have impaired reproduction. Mosses accumulate this heavy metal from the atmosphere and are often used as biological monitors of airborne lead.

Substance	Sources	Hazards/Toxity

LEAD
(continued)
		(0.00003 oz) without suffering toxic effects. Prolonged regular exposure, even to moderate levels of lead, can precipitate symptoms such as:
		
		    alterations in brain waves and EEGs
		    alterations in nerve performance
		    altered behaviour in young children
		    anaemia (high exposure)
		    constipation
		    decreased mental development in children
		    depression and emotional disturbances
		    fatigue
		    high blood pressure
		    irritability
		    joint pains
		    loss of appetite
		    stomach pains
		
		Lead is highly toxic if swallowed or inhaled. The symptoms of acute lead toxicity include brain and spinal cord disruption. Lead can also affect the liver, kidneys, cardiovascular system, heart, immune system and normal blood production. Sperm count and formation may be affected in men exposed to high levels of lead.
		    Lead is included in the Environmental Protection Agency (EPA) list of 'priority pollutants' classified as hazardous to human health.

Protection	Impact on Environment/Wildlife

garden away from a busy road as some of the lead in the air will be taken up by the crops. Avoid eating berries and other items from the roadside. If you suspect that your soil is contaminated with lead, arrange for a soil analysis. Contact: Institute of Environmental Health Officers, Chadwick House, Rushworth Street, London, SE1 0QT, Telephone (071) 928 6006.

Lead from vehicle exhaust is deposited on fruit and vegetables displayed close to busy traffic areas. If you buy unwrapped fruit from open stalls wash it well in warm water to which two tablespoons of vinegar have been added. Vinegar acidifies the water and helps to remove some of the wax and heavy metals.

To ensure that your children's toys are safe, look for the Toy and Hobby Manufacturers Association British Standards Lion Mark. For more information contact: The British Toy and Hobby Manufacturers Association, 80 Camberwell Road, London, SE5 0EG, Telephone (071) 701 7271 — or: British Standards Institution, Education Department, Linford Wood, Milton Keynes, MK14 6LE, Telephone (0908) 220022.

A diet low in calcium, vitamin D and iron will encourage the body to take up ingested lead, and some vegans or vegetarians may be more vulnerable, especially if vitamin D is in short supply during the winter. Lead interferes with calcium and zinc in the body and many symptoms of zinc deficiency are the same as symptoms of too much lead. An adequate intake and absorption of vitamin B_1 may help to prevent the deposition of lead in body tissue. If this is taken in supplement form it must be accompanied by vitamin B complex. (For more details on vitamins and minerals and their sources see Chapter 7.)

It has been suggested that a fairly

Substance	Sources	Hazards/Toxity
LEAD (continued)		
LINDANE	garden and household pesticides home wood treatments woodworm treatments	Only the gamma HCH form of lindane is permitted for use within the EEC; gamma BHC is banned. Lindane is banned completely in five countries (Sweden, Japan, Singapore, Hungary and Ecuador) and in New Zealand is permitted for use only by licensed professionals. It is banned in the USA in vaporizers and indoor smoke fumigation products. In the UK it is freely available. Lindane becomes more toxic in a warmer environment, i.e. in the home, especially if heated. It belongs to the same chemical family as DDT (chlorinated hydrocarbons) and is a potent irritant to skin, eyes and breathing passages. It may also cause allergic reactions. In extremely high concentrations, higher

Protection	Impact on Environment/Wildlife
high protein and low fat diet is helpful and that yogurt and high pectin fruits (apples, damsons, bananas), seaweeds, garlic, onions, beans and algin from seaweed will help the body to eliminate ingested lead. Vitamin C is a powerful anti-toxicant which neutralizes lead's toxic effects, and lecithin contains the sulphurous amino acid, methionine, which removes lead from the tissues. A diet deficient in protein, chromium, manganese, calcium and zinc increases the body's vulnerability to the toxic effects of lead. Alcohol increases lead's absorption in the body and smoking can increase lead intake by 25 percent.	

If using lindane indoors, and this is not recommended, use protective clothing and wear a breathing mask. Ensure excellent ventilation. Spraying is more dangerous than painting because tiny droplets are suspended in the air and easily breathed into the lungs. When using lindane in the loft ensure that all water tanks are completely sealed.
 	
    It is recommended that an area treated with lindane should not be entered for 48 hours; however, a *Which?* report (April 1989) disclosed research which showed that the concentrations of lindane in the air of a treated building are relatively low for the first week after treatment and then rise to the maximum levels during the next four weeks. It is advisable to avoid home wood treatments during the winter when heat and bad ventilation encourage lindane to vaporize and seriously contaminate indoor air.
 	
    Preferably avoid the use of hazardous chemicals in the garden, or at least exercise great caution while using lindane. Keep pets and children well clear of the treated area for at least two weeks. Cats are the most vulnerable animals to lindane poisoning as they
	Gamma HCH is a persistent chemical which is now widespread in the environment. Bees and fish are threatened and the chemical is toxic to humans and other mammals including bats. It has a delayed negative effect on pheasant egg laying.

Substance	Sources	Hazards/Toxity
LINDANE (continued)		than those typically found during or after the use of home wood treatments, poisoning has resulted, causing effects ranging from fatigue, headache and difficulty sleeping to more serious reactions including convulsions. People with an inherited metabolic defect involving glucose-6-phosphate dehydrogenase are reportedly more vulnerable to the toxic effects of this chemical. There have been several cases of aplastic anaemia or a similar blood condition developing in people exposed to extremely high levels of all forms of lindane.
MERCURY	barometers (if broken) batteries coal burning dental amalgam fillings fluorescent light tubes golf balls (centre portion) lawn treatments (calomel) thermometers (if broken) UV lamps* (if broken)	Mercury is an extremely toxic heavy metal which is most dangerous when inhaled or absorbed through the skin. It is a cumulative poison which is retained in the tissues and builds up with repeated exposure. Mercury emits dangerous fumes when heated and the metal is dangerous in warm, unventilated areas. If absorbed during pregnancy mercury can cause birth defects. Symptoms of mercury poisoning range from excess salivation, fatigue, reduced hearing and vision, vertigo, irritability,

*These contain mercury vapour which could be hazardous if broken in a confined or badly ventilated area.

Protection	Impact on Environment/Wildlife
are not able to remove the chemical from their systems. Avoid burning wood treated with lindane on bonfires or in the grate at home as the highly toxic gas phosgene is released. In February 1989 121 MPs called for a ban on lindane. The Government replied that providing wood preservatives are used in the correct way they do not present a hazard to health.	
If a thermometer breaks, the mercury should only be picked up using rubber gloves. Children must be prevented from touching or playing with it. Mercury should be disposed of in a well labelled bag in the dustbin. Ensure that children or animals will not have access to the bin. If you use a vacuum cleaner to pick up spilled mercury it will vaporize, and mercury is more toxic when inhaled in this form. Never give a dog a golf ball to play with as the centre contains mercury; once unwound the centre is dangerous to children who then also have access to the poison. If a barometer or any item containing a significant quantity of mercury is broken, the room must be ventilated immediately and children and animals kept out. Contact your closest	Mercury does not break down in the environment and is now listed in the Government 'Red List' and the EC List I 'Black List' of chemicals considered to be so toxic, persistent or bio-accumulative in the environment that steps should be taken to eliminate pollution by them.

Substance	Sources	Hazards/Toxity
MERCURY (continued)		moodiness and depression to more serious symptoms including loss of coordination and intellectual ability, psychosis, and kidney damage. It also affects the nervous system and the body's immune function by suppressing the production of T-lymphocytes which are produced mainly by the thymus gland. It usually takes the body approximately 70 days to flush out about half the mercury it has been exposed to. The term 'mad as a hatter' originated from the mental disturbances exhibited by nineteenth-century hat makers. They were constantly exposed to mercury as they dipped felt into mercuric nitrate to soften it.
METHYLCHLOROFORM see 1,1,1 -TRICHLOROETHANE		
METHYLENE CHLORIDE (dichloromethane)	colour sprays for leather decaffeinated coffee and tea some hair sprays paint removers and solvents shoe polish synthetic turpentine It is also found in more than 50 percent of 1200 products tested by the US Environmental Protection Agency (EPA).	Methylene chloride is a chlorinated hydrocarbon solvent. It is a carcinogen taken into the body mainly by inhalation. Normal indoor concentrations are unmeasured, but it is estimated that using paint stripper for 8 hours in a badly ventilated area is equivalent to a lifetime's normal exposure. It is moderately toxic and high air concentrations cause dizziness, lethargy and

Protection	Impact on Environment/Wildlife

environmental health department as you should not handle the mercury.

Fluorescent light tubes contain mercury vapour and great care should be taken not to break them, especially indoors. Mercury vapour is particularly toxic.

Under EC law mercury may still be used in a lawn treatment product for clubroot and dollar spot. We recommend that you read labels and avoid it.

Batteries are available which contain no mercury and no cadmium. These are the best choice for the sake of the environment.

Selenium protects the body against mercury poisoning and numerous supplements can be used to help pick up and carry mercury from the system, particularly before, during and after dental amalgam removal or after an old amalgam filling has been removed and replaced. The specific supplements are vitamin C, L-cysteine, selenium, L-glutathione, kelp, garlic, a multiple mineral complex, vitamin E, chlorella and acidophilus. If you are allergic to sulphur do not take L-cysteine.

Only use paint strippers or solvents indoors if the area is extremely well ventilated. It is advisable not to strip paint in a bedroom and then sleep in the room, especially in the winter when windows are closed and the heating is on. (See Chapter 7 for more information on how to protect the body against chemical pollution.) Seek medical attention if methylene chloride gets onto skin or in the eyes and causes burning or injury. Wash the area for a prolonged period with large quantities of clean water.

Methylene chloride is highly flammable and products which contain

No data found, but all solvents should be used only when absolutely necessary. Because of their widespread use, their disposal may pose environmental problems.

Substance	Sources	Hazards/Toxity
METHYLENE CHLORIDE (continued)		tiredness, especially with prolonged exposure. People with heart disease may suffer particularly adverse effects if exposed to this chemical. It is a powerful skin irritant (note its use as a caustic paint stripper!) and can cause skin burns.
MOULDS AND FUNGI	old books damp areas in buildings house plants	Sensitive individuals may develop allergies if exposed to moulds and fungi. The symptoms can include: coughing breathing difficulties eye, throat and respiratory irritation nausea fever

Protection	Impact on Environment/Wildlife

Protection

it should only be used where there is no danger of combustion. If burned, the vapour is highly toxic.

Chlorinated hydrocarbons are particularly toxic to cats; if used the family pet should be extricated to a safe area.

Avoid cheap brands of coffee as they are likely to be decaffeinated with solvent chemicals; preferably choose organically grown coffee if you drink it. At the time of writing the following brands are decaffeinated *without* solvent:

Instant	*Filter*
Café Hag	Kenco
Choice	
Gold Blend	*Teabags*
Kenco	Luaka
M&S freeze dried	
Maxwell House	
Nescafé	

Decaffeinated coffee has been linked with a rise in cholesterol levels, since stronger coffee beans are used to produce a good flavour. Coffee contains hundreds of chemicals besides caffeine and the cardiac stimulant theobromine, but it has not yet been determined which one is responsible for raising cholesterol levels.

When buying old property or a basement flat, check the walls and ceilings very carefully for signs of mould, dry rot or fungi. Also beware of freshly decorated walls – they may be temporarily covering a problem area.

Mix borax with plain wallpaper paste to inhibit the growth of mould. If you are sensitive to moulds place a layer of crushed stones on top of the soil around houseplants – it will help to inhibit its growth. Avoid using wicker baskets as plant holders as they may harbour moulds.

Impact on Environment/Wildlife

Not applicable.

Substance	Sources	Hazards/Toxity
MOULDS AND FUNGI (continued)		
NAPHTHALENE	carpet and upholstery shampoos car upholstery correction fluid dry-cleaning fluids glass cleaners glues mothballs stain removers wallpaper cleaners	Naphthalene is a suspected cancer-causing agent in humans and is poisonous if swallowed, inhaled or absorbed through the skin. Symptoms of toxic exposure can include headache, nausea, vomiting, excessive perspiration and confusion. Extreme exposure could be fatal. Naphthalene is included in the Environmental Protection Agency (EPA) list of 'priority pollutants' classified as hazardous to human health.
NITROGEN DIOXIDE	bottled-gas heaters cigarette smoke gas appliances gas cookers laser printers paraffin heaters	Britain's air regularly exceeds the World Health Organization's safe guidelines for nitrogen dioxide. Levels inside the home may also be quite

Protection	Impact on Environment/Wildlife
Sunshine is naturally antibacterial. Rugs, mattresses and bedding can be placed in the sun for a couple of hours twice a week to prevent the growth of bacteria and moulds. The treatments used to kill dry rot, moulds and fungi contain **formaldehyde** as well as several other chemicals to which some people are sensitive. If you are having your home treated try to arrange to be away for several days so that you are not exposed to high levels of the chemicals. Ventilate the area as well as possible. Extractor fans, plenty of ventilation, full-spectrum lights and ionizers can help to prevent the growth of mould in areas where the problem is due to condensation. For details see the end of this chapter and Chapter 8.	
It is best to avoid products containing naphthalene where possible, but when used it should be in a well ventilated area and care should be taken to avoid skin contact. Mothballs are an unnecessary source of this chemical — there are many alternative moth repellants, including cedar. Moth eggs can be killed by laying clothes in the sun or putting them in a warm cycle in a dryer and then storing them in a sealed container. For more information see the end of this chapter.	Naphthalene is toxic to fish and other aquatic life, even in low concentrations.
Even correctly serviced gas cookers can emit levels of nitrogen dioxide which may affect health. Ventilate all areas where gas appliances are used, and if necessary locate an extractor fan close to the stove. Nitrogen dioxide levels in	Nitrogen dioxide is one of the major pollutants from power stations and vehicles and is a major contributor to the production of acid rain which leads to loss of trees and forests, and poisoning of fish in lakes where

Substance	Sources	Hazards/Toxity
NITROGEN DIOXIDE (continued)	photocopiers (nitrous oxides) power station emissions vehicle exhaust	high, especially if there are numerous gas appliances and ventilation is inadequate. Nitrogen oxides, like carbon monoxide, bind with haemoglobin and may damage the respiratory system, weaken the immune system and contribute to the development of bronchitis or emphysema. Exposure may also affect the brain and nervous system causing depression and slower reactions. Young children, the elderly and those who suffer from bronchitis or asthma are most vulnerable to respiratory illness induced by exposure to nitrogen oxides. This is in part due to a significant inhibition of the important prostaglandin-metabolizing function of the lungs. It is also possible that heavy smokers are more vulnerable. Research indicates that children living in homes where gas is used for cooking tend to have more coughs, colds and bronchitis than those from homes where the cooker is electric. Methyl mercaptan, the chemical used to give gas its odour, is also toxic.
OZONE	electrical items with bad connections electrical sparking	Ozone is a poisonous blue allotrope of oxygen with a pungent, irritating

Protection	Impact on Environment/Wildlife
kitchens with gas stoves can often be higher than those found in the air near traffic. The United States National Institute of Safety and Health (NIOSH) has run evaluations of photocopiers and found that as well as nitrogen oxides they also emit very low levels of **ozone, carbon monoxide, ammonium,** and **selenium oxide.** Vitamins A, C, E and selenium protect the cells against oxidizing pollutants. Vitamin E specifically protects the body against nitrogen oxides. Nitrogen dioxide is responsible for a large percentage of acid rain. At low quantities it stimulates plant growth, but it also weakens the plant making it more vulnerable to frost damage and insect attack.	the soil contains aluminium. When hydrocarbons and nitrogen dioxide from vehicle exhaust mix in the lower atmosphere they contribute to the generation of ozone and other pollutants. See *acid rain* and *hydrocarbons* in the glossary for more information.
If you own an ionizer which produces ozone (none of the newer models do this) it is advisable to replace it with	Ozone in the lower atmosphere is thought to be another contributory factor in the loss of trees and forests in

Substance	Sources	Hazards/Toxity
OZONE (continued)	high-voltage electrical equipment laser printers old ozone-producing ionizers photocopiers smog vehicle exhaust (causes the production of ozone)	odour. It is naturally present in air, especially around the sea, but excessive levels can detrimentally affect health. It is also formed by certain electrical equipment and electrical sparking, and by a photochemical reaction between sunlight, nitrogen oxides and hydrocarbons. The highest levels occur during hot weather and when traffic is heavy. Respiratory infections and lowered immune response are major effects of ozone exposure, and it is associated with production of free radicals in the body. Concentrations as low as 1 part per million can cause nausea, difficulty breathing and chest pains. Long-term exposure can result in stiffer, less efficient lungs, causing permanent shortness of breath, making further exposure to ozone more dangerous. A very high level of free radicals damages cells and RNA and DNA, the material for a cell's genetic blueprint. Free radicals contribute to rapid premature aging by damaging the skin's collagen and cells, and can also cause damage to arteries and depress the hormone which regulates blood clotting.

Protection	Impact on Environment/Wildlife
one of the models available from the manufacturers listed in Chapter 8. If you work in a badly ventilated office close to a photocopier or laser printer which is always switched on, you may be exposed to ozone on a regular basis. [*Note*: Some machines are fitted with ozone filters, but as these become ineffective after a few thousand copies they should be changed regularly.] As a protective measure ensure that your daily diet contains adequate quantities of vitamins C and E. A deficiency of either may increase susceptibility to damage caused by air pollution and ozone. Vitamin E plays an important role by protecting red blood cells against free radical stress from ozone exposure; the absence of vitamin E exacerbates lung injury from ozone inhalation. PABA (para-aminobenzoic acid), a member of the B complex vitamins, provides protection against ozone toxicity. Vitamin A and the mineral selenium work with other nutrients to protect the body against free radical damage. More details on free radical damage can be found in Chapter 7.	West Germany as it has a harmful effect on vegetation. It is also included in the list of 'greenhouse' gases since it is present as a pollutant in the lower atmosphere.

Substance	Sources	Hazards/Toxity
PENTACHLOROPHENOL (PCP, Sodium penta-chlorophenate)	chipboard/plywood wood preservatives and treatments	Exposure to pentachlorophenol may cause eye and mucous membrane irritation, coughing, breathing difficulty, loss of appetite, sweating. Chronic exposure has been linked with kidney and liver damage and it has caused severe skin rashes. Extreme exposure has been known to cause convulsions and may prove fatal. It is a teratogen and a possible carcinogen in animals. It is extremely toxic if swallowed, inhaled or absorbed through the skin, and may also have negative effects on the immune system. There have been reports of it reducing sperm count in men. Its toxicity is compounded by the presence of dioxins (see glossary) in some products, and when burned it produces toxic fumes. Pentachlorophenol is included in the Environmental Protection Agency (EPA) list of 'priority pollutants' classified as hazardous to human health, and the EPA has banned its use in inhabited buildings in the US.
PERCHLOROETHYLENE (tetrachloroethylene)	dry-cleaning fluids household cleaning products	This chemical is an animal carcinogen. Different levels of

Protection	Impact on Environment/Wildlife
Use these products only in the open air. Preferably use natural wood preservatives — see Chapter 8 for details. If a building has been treated with products containing pentachlorophenol, it is not safe to return to it for at least 24 hours — many experts think much longer — and ventilation should be a priority for several months after treatment, especially if the building is occupied by the very young or old.	Dioxins are synthesized when pentachlorophenol is made (see glossary). Pentachlorophenol is harmful to fish and other aquatic life and appears on the Government 'Red List' and the EC List I 'Black List' of chemicals considered to be so toxic, persistent or bio-accumulative in the environment that steps should be taken to eliminate pollution by them.
Perchloroethylene can accumulate in the body, and people who work with it should ensure extremely good	Perchloroethylene is toxic to fish and other aquatic life even in low concentrations.

Substance	Sources	Hazards/Toxity
PERCHLOROETHYLENE (continued)	shoe polish stain removers	exposure may cause a range of symptoms such as dizziness, fatigue, nausea, loss of appetite and disorientation. It may also cause liver damage. It is moderately toxic if swallowed, absorbed through the skin or if the vapours are inhaled. The vapours can also cause throat and eye irritation and produce drowsiness. Repeated exposure may lead to skin conditions such as dermatitis. If heated, further toxic fumes are produced. Elimination from the body is slow due to progressive release from adipose (fat) tissue.
PERMETHRIN	household/garden insecticides wood preservatives woodworm treatments	Permethrin is moderately toxic if swallowed and is an eye and skin irritant. It has been listed as a possible cancer-causing agent by the Food and Drug Administration in the USA, but it is cleared by the Nature Conservancy Council as safe for use in areas where bats breed due to its low toxicity in mammals.
PHENOLS	chipboard creosote disinfectants paint paint removers plywood printer's ink	Phenols are corrosive aromatic compounds (see glossary) that can cause a range of symptoms depending upon the exposure. There may be severe skin or eye irritations, or more serious illness including liver and kidney damage,

Protection	Impact on Environment/Wildlife
ventilation. It can be passed on through breast milk, and can be dangerous to the baby if the mother is exposed to high levels. Dry-cleaned items should always be well aired outside for at least 24 hours before being stored in a bedroom, especially in the winter when the ventilation is likely to be inadequate. When bringing dry-cleaned items home in the car, ensure that the windows are open. Allow continental quilts to air for at least two days after dry-cleaning before sleeping under them. Down and other fillings tend to 'hold' vaporous chemicals in large quantities. Limit the dry-cleaning of clothes as much as possible.	
Organic (plant based) wood treatments are available from AURO and LIVOS; both companies are listed in Chapter 8 (p.266). Alternative insecticides appear in Chapter 4. If using this chemical, keep the application to a minimum and protect skin and eyes.	This chemical is extremely dangerous to fish and will kill bees.
Avoid contact with as many sources of phenols as possible. If using products like paint or paint removers, ensure that the ventilation is adequate during use and for at least 24 hours after completing the work. If the chemical is to be used in an area like the bedroom or living room it is best left until the weather becomes warm enough to open windows. Confine the use of	Phenols are dangerous to fish and other aquatic life.

Substance	Sources	Hazards/Toxity
PHENOLS (continued)		vomiting and circulatory collapse. Phenol can cause death if swallowed, and if heated produces toxic fumes. It is easily absorbed through the lungs and skin and if splashed on the skin rapidly affects the nervous sytem. It is excreted in the urine within about 24 hours.
PHENOTHRIN see PYRETHROIDS		
PLASTICS acrylonitril butadiene styrene (ABS plastic)	appliances, car bumpers, food tubs and lids etc.	All plastics 'outgas' fumes whether detectable or not, especially when heated. Soft plastics release more plasticizer than harder ones. A NASA study found that **polyester** released the most fumes — this is particularly noticeable when ironing polyester clothing. It may cause respiratory tract and eye irritation or dermatitis.
blown polystyrene	egg boxes, fast food trays, polystyrene protective packaging material etc.	
nylon	fabrics, cords/ropes, etc.	
polyester	polyester fabrics, 'poly' cotton fabrics	
polyethylene (polythene) low density	soft plastics such as sacks, bin liners, carrier bags, detergent bottles, etc.	Benzene and phenol are used to make **nylon**, and some individuals may be particularly sensitive to this material even though only tiny quantities of these substances remain in the finished item.
polyethylene (polythene) high density	hard plastics such as those used for bottle caps and bottling pharmaceutical products, disinfectant, milk and fruit juice, etc.	**Polyvinylpyrolidone (PVP)** is in hair sprays, and inhalation may cause lung disease (thesaurosis) with enlarged lymph nodes and changes in blood cells.
polyethylene terephthalate (PET)	oven-ready meal trays, soda bottles, etc.	**Polytetrafluorethylene**, or Teflon, produces poisonous and irritating gases when burned, and to a lesser degree during
polymerized thermoplastic vinyl compounds	paints	

Protection	Impact on Environment/Wildlife

creosote to outdoors only and use with caution. Protect the skin and eyes and always wear gloves when using creosote and other chemicals containing phenols.

Harder plastics are less likely to emit vapours than the soft plastics and these usually have no perceptible smell. It may take up to two years before the outgassing of chemicals diminishes from most soft plastics — if you can still smell it, it is still outgassing. NASA banned PVCs from use in the space capsules due to problems caused by vinyl chloride vapours.

Choose alternatives to plastics whenever possible. PVC products to be brought into the home should be 'aired' for several weeks in an area that will not contaminate the indoor environment, or at least placed in a very well ventilated locality. If PVC tiles are laid, ventilate the area well until the odour has subsided.

Use clingfilm that is free of plasticizer and PVC to prevent the migration of plasticizer into fatty foods like cheese, butter, meat. Preferably cover food with a plate rather than clingfilm when microwaving. Wait for food to cool before transferring it to plastic containers for storage. Never burn any plastic item in the fireplace, as the chemicals released, including **toluene diisocyanate**, can be highly toxic and cause damage to the lungs.

Plastics made from cellulose rather

There are more than 50 types of plastic made from various raw materials including coal and oil. Many new plastics are being researched and tested, especially those which are photo- and biodegradable and others which are currently being developed from plant cellulose. Most ordinary plastics (with the exception of PET which breaks down in the environment very slowly) do not biodegrade and will remain in land-fill sites when other materials have broken down, but many are recyclable and every year approximately 150,000 tonnes of plastic wastes are recovered. There will be many plastic recycling projects around the country in the coming years.

Plasticizers may contaminate water and are persistent in the environment.

Substance	Sources	Hazards/Toxity
polypropylene	food packaging tubs, wrapping film for biscuits and crisps, microwavable trays, etc.	heating. Teflon or PTFE coatings have been used as a covering for roofs and walls, but because they release highly toxic fumes when incinerated, i.e.
polystyrene	yogurt pots, clear egg cartons, bottle caps, etc.	burned at extremely high temperatures, their use has virtually been stopped. **Epoxy resins** are suspected
polytetrafluorethylene (PTFE)	Teflon	carcinogens, and **polythene** is a suspected cancer-causing agent.
polyurethane	foams in furniture, pillows, mattresses, (nearly 90 percent of furniture is filled with polyurethane foam), paint, varnishes etc.	**PVC** is a potent carcinogen which is also known to cause birth defects and genetic changes. It releases vinyl chloride (**vinyl chloride monomer** is the raw
polyvinyl chloride (PVC)	shower curtains, babies' plastic pants, food trays, lids, cake and sandwich packs, car seats, DIY blister packs, clingfilm etc.	material from which PVC is made) especially when new. The odour is particularly strong − for instance, the smell of a new shower curtain, or plastic in a new car,
polyvinylpyrolidone (PVP)	hair sprays, setting gels	particularly on a hot day. Symptoms of toxic
thermoplastic/setting resins	melamine	exposure to vinyl chloride include allergic skin
vinyl chloride monomer (VCM)	raw material from which PVC is made	reactions, breathing difficulties, digestive
	Other products containing plastics include correction fluids, epoxy resins, chewing gum, wood varnishes and finishes.	upsets, dryness of mucous membranes in the nose and mouth, numbness and tremors. Hepatitis and chronic bronchitis have also been recorded as linked to vinyl chloride. In addition, PVCs and other polymers contain a group of chemicals called plasticizers that make them stronger and more flexible. The most widely used plasticizer in Britain is dioctyl phthalate, a chemical capable of

Protection	Impact on Environment/Wildlife
than coal or petroleum are safer. They are manufactured mainly from cotton fibres or wood and are used to make items such as frames for glasses, toothbrush handles, steering wheels, bodies for pens, and typewriter keys.	

Substance	Sources	Hazards/Toxity
PLASTICS (continued)		causing cancer and damage to a developing foetus in animals. Plasticizers have been taken out of a number of brands of clingfilm because they can migrate from the packaging into foods, especially meats and cheese which have a high fat content. **Vinyl chloride** is released from the very soft plastics, and is the most dangerous chemical, especially when burned. The fumes are highly toxic and contain hydrogen chloride, dioxins and phosgene. Burning **polyurethane**, acrylic, **melamine** and other plastics containing nitrogen produces hydrogen cyanide, and burning **polyurethane foam** also releases **toluene diisocyanate.** PVC and acrylonitrile are included in the Environmental Protection Agency (EPA) list of 'priority pollutants' classified as hazardous to human health.
PYRETHROIDS	synthetic insecticides, woodworm treatments and wood preservatives based on plant-derived pyrethrum: allethrin alphacypermethrin* bioallethrin bioresmethrin* deltamethrin*	Skin contact with **allethrin** may cause contact dermatitis. **Bioallethrin** is highly toxic if swallowed. **Bioresmethrin** is highly toxic if inhaled, and moderately so if absorbed through the skin or swallowed. If inhaled, **phenothrin** is moderately toxic. **Resmethrin**

*For household and garden use by professionals only; not for general sale.

Protection	Impact on Environment/Wildlife
If heated, both allethrin and phenothrin produce acrid and irritant fumes. As with all chemicals, care should be taken to protect the skin and eyes.	All pyrethroids are toxic to fish and harmful to bees. However, their persistence in the environment is low and some are considered safe for use in roofs inhabited by bats.

Substance	Sources	Hazards/Toxity
	phenothrin resmethrin tetramethrin	inhalation is likely to be more harmful than ingestion although absorption through the skin could also be dangerous. **Tetramethrin** has slight to moderate toxicity if swallowed. Some pyrethroids are suspected carcinogens in animals.
PYRETHRUM	household and garden insecticide	If swallowed or inhaled, pyrethrum is moderately toxic. Sensitive people may find that inhaling pyrethrum triggers asthmatic-type breathing. However, its effects are short-lived due to its rapid detoxification in the body. Piperonyl butoxide may be added to pyrethrin insecticides to increase their activity; this chemical is highly toxic if absorbed through the skin.
RADIATION	air travel cosmic rays granite* gypsum high-tension powerlines hospitals luminous clock and watch dials nuclear industry phosphogypsum satellite dishes some smoke detectors†	Scientists are more concerned about the long-term effects associated with exposure to radiation as its risks tend to be cumulative. The main dangers from prolonged exposure are cancers, primarily those of the lungs and respiratory system and the reproductive organs.

*Homes built with, or on, granite — some areas of Cornwall, Devon, Derbyshire, or Yorkshire. This form of radiation is known as radon.
†Ionization type which contain americium-241. Photoelectric smoke detectors are a safe alternative.

Protection	Impact on Environment/Wildlife
Pyrethrum is a natural plant derivative but it should still be handled with care as skin contact can cause allergic dermatitis.	Pyrethrum's persistence in the environment is extremely brief and it can be used safely without harming bees; however, in common with synthetic pyrethroids, it is very toxic to fish. The organic standards set by the Soil Association permit the use of pyrethrum under certain circumstances.
For detailed information on radon, radiation, and geopathic stress see Chapter 6.	Radiation is naturally present in cosmic rays and in rocks and soils in the environment. The only threat from radiation such as fallout from nuclear testing and nuclear accidents is to human and animal life. Strontium-90, a breakdown product of radiation, is extremely persistent in the soil.

Substance	Sources	Hazards/Toxity
RADIATION (continued)	tobacco smoke TV sets (very little emitted from the newer TVs) VDUs X-rays	
RESMETHRIN see PYRETHROIDS		
SELENIUM OXIDE	electronic calculators photocopiers with selenium plates photographic exposure meters solar cells	Exposure to toxic levels of selenium may result in a decreased sense of taste or smell, respiratory disorders, skin rash, irritability, fatigue.
SODIUM HYDROXIDE	oven cleaners	Sodium hydroxide is also known as caustic soda. It is an irritant and corrosive chemical which is very toxic if swallowed and dangerous if it gets into the eyes. Oven cleaning aerosols containing this chemical are particularly dangerous.
SODIUM PENTACHLOROPHENATE see PENTACHLOROPHENOL		

Protection	Impact on Environment/Wildlife
The United States Institute of Safety and Health (NIOSH) has run evaluations on photocopiers and found them to emit very low levels of **ozone, carbon monoxide, ammonium, nitrogen oxides** and selenium. Mild selenium poisoning can be offset with sulphurous foods such as onions, garlic, cabbage and eggs. Also sulphur, amino acids such as L-cysteine, and methionine.	Selenium oxide is toxic to animals and may cause reproductive problems in farm animals.
Always ventilate the kitchen well if it does become necessary to use chemical oven cleaners, and rinse the oven extremely well afterwards. Use rubber gloves to protect your skin and prevent chemical absorption. Vitamin C is a general detoxifier and if fumes have been inhaled it may be helpful in reducing levels of the chemical in the body. Provided you are not taking specific medications (see Chapter 7), 500 mg of vitamin C can be taken every 2 hours until the mild respiratory symptoms subside. For severe exposure a doctor should always be consulted before self-treatment is attempted.	No data found.

Substance	Sources	Hazards/Toxity
SULPHUR DIOXIDE	burning of fuels such as coal and oil gas stoves gas appliances factory emissions food preservative power station emissions vehicle exhaust	In the home, levels of sulphur dioxide may build up in badly ventilated rooms, and for people suffering from respiratory complaints (asthma or bronchitis), angina or sensitivity to petrochemicals (especially the elderly) this can be a serious threat to health. Low concentrations of combustion chemicals have a negative impact on health, even though the effects are subtle and sometimes difficult to associate with exposure. By-products of gas appliances also include **formaldehyde**, various oxides, **carbon monoxide** and hydrogen cyanide.
TALCUM	additive in some foods baby powders cosmetics and face powders dusting powders filler in some paints and plastics filler in some vitamin/mineral tablets paper coating	Talc is a mineral and is often found mixed with asbestos. It is not clear whether the hazardous effects of using talc are from asbestos or the talc itself. Its particles are flat or fibrous and occur as a very fine dust with some particles so small that an electron microscope is needed to see them. These smaller particles constitute a danger when breathed in. Once in the lungs talc is not removed by the body's natural mechanisms and may build up in the tissues. The *Journal of the*

Protection	Impact on Environment/Wildlife
It is important to ventilate well all rooms where a gas appliance of any kind is in use. See the guidelines which appear under the entry for **carbon monoxide** for more information on gas appliance safety. Evidence shows that all-electric homes have far lower concentrations of combustion by-products. Sulphur in the air decreases the body's B complex vitamins.	Since the introduction of the Clean Air Acts, levels of sulphur dioxide in British cities from coal fireplaces has decreased, but vehicle exhaust gases have increased. The burning of fossil fuels such as coal and oil releases literally millions of tons of sulphur dioxide into the environment every year. Reactions which take place in the atmosphere between moisture and gases released from vehicles, industry and power stations (especially sulphur and nitrogen dioxide) result in the production of sulphuric acid — the caustic component of acid rain. Acid rain and **ozone** are linked with the destruction of and damage to trees in West Germany. Acid rain also causes aluminium to be leached out of the soil in and around rivers and lakes, and this affects the aquatic environment by killing fish and birds which feed on water insects. Concentrations which animals can tolerate do serious damage to some forms of plant life.
The case reported is extremely rare, but because inhaled talcum is not excreted from the lungs it would be wise to limit its use, especially for babies and small children. Talc should always be kept out of their reach. If you are in the habit of applying talc with a powder puff it is safer to switch to a talc-free type. Alternative talc-free dusting powders are available from some health stores and from several mail order companies listed in Chapter 8.	Not applicable.

Substance	Sources	Hazards/Toxity
TALCUM (continued)		*American Medical Association* reported a case of severe respiratory disease (pulmonary talcosis) which an autopsy revealed had been caused by deposits of talc in the lobes of both lungs. There is also some concern about the inclusion of talc in some foods and in a number of vitamin tablets – it has a possible link with the development of intestinal disease.
TETRACHLOROETHY-LENE see **PERCHLOROETHYLENE**		
TETRAMETHRIN see **PYRETHROIDS**		
TOLUENE DIISOCYANATE	burning plastics cleaning products damp treatment dry-cleaning fluids glues and adhesives nail polish paint removers paint thinners pens and markers polyurethane printer's ink stain removers	Inhaling smoke from burning or heated **plastics** is complicated by the release of toluene diisocyanate. For some people this can cause coughing and skin or eye irritation. Those who are particularly sensitive may find that the polyurethane foam in furnishings releases enough of the chemical to cause these symptoms without burning. Toluene is moderately toxic if inhaled and long-term exposure may adversely affect the central nervous system and brain leading to mental changes,

Protection	Impact on Environment/Wildlife
Damp treatments and glues are manufactured using this solvent; if used in the home the area should be extremely well ventilated. If absorbed through the skin toluene is less toxic than when inhaled, but care should be taken to avoid skin contact. Toluene is a slight fire hazard. Vitamin C is a general detoxifier and if fumes have accidentally been inhaled it can be helpful to reduce levels of the chemical in the body. Provided you are not taking specific medications (see Chapter 7), 500 mg of vitamin C can be taken every 2 hours until the symptoms subside. For severe exposure a doctor should always be consulted before self-treatment is attempted.	No data found, but all solvents should be used only when absolutely necessary. Because of their widespread use their disposal may pose environmental problems.

Substance	Sources	Hazards/Toxity
TOLUENE DIISOCYANATE (continued)		depression, disorientation, irritability, and liver and kidney damage. It is also mutagenic. Toluene is included in the Environmental Protection Agency (EPA) list of 'priority pollutants' classified as hazardous to human health.
TRIBUTYLTIN OXIDE (TBTO)	masonry biocide wood preservative pesticides	TBTO may be absorbed through the skin and is an eye irritant. It is highly toxic if swallowed and may negatively affect the immune system.
1,1,1-TRICHLORO-ETHANE (methyl chloroform)	some adhesives correction fluids (except Opti and non-solvent fluids) degreasers printing processes shoe polish spray mount stain removers suede and leather protection sprays	This solvent is widely used and is classified as having low to moderate toxicity if inhaled or swallowed. High concentrations (particularly if inhaled) produce narcotic effects. Very high concentrations may lead to heart attack. It has been linked with birth defects and miscarriage. Long-term exposure can affect the central nervous system causing psychological disturbances. It is a severe eye irritant and mild skin irritant.

Protection	Impact on Environment/Wildlife
Avoid using products containing TBTO. Since 31 October 1990 this chemical is no longer permitted in DIY products.	TBTO appears on the Government 'Red List' and the EC List I 'Black List' of chemicals considered to be so toxic, persistent or bio-accumulative in the environment that steps should be taken to eliminate pollution by them. Products containing this chemical MUST be disposed of safely. For advice please contact your local council. Disposing of products containing TBTO in the dustbin or down the drain could result in TBTO contaminating drinking water supplies and infiltrating the food chain.
Only use this chemical in a well ventilated area and avoid breathing the fumes. If trichloroethane gets into the eyes they should be rinsed for a prolonged period with clean water; a doctor should be consulted if the irritation persists. Naked lights and smoking in a room where this chemical is being used may cause it to burn and release highly toxic phosgene gas. Vitamin C is a general detoxifier and if fumes have been accidentally inhaled it can be helpful in reducing levels of the chemical in the body. Provided you are not taking specific medications (see Chapter 7), 500 mg of vitamin C can be taken every 2 hours until the symptoms subside. For chronic exposure a doctor should always be consulted before self-treatment is attempted.	Trichloroethane is persistent in the environment and can leach into water supplies. It is a serious air pollutant which produces atmospheric chlorine and causes destruction of the ozone layer.

Substance	Sources	Hazards/Toxity
TRICHLOROETHYLENE (also known as 'trike')	degreasers some DIY products drinking water contaminant some dry-cleaning solvents extraction solvent for oils and waxes fragrances fumigants hot water vapour household cleaning products paints some pesticides as an 'inert' ingredient refrigerant shoe polish stain removers	Trichloroethylene is a hydrocarbon solvent to which addiction has been recorded. It is lipid-soluble and easily gets across cell membranes where it can disturb intercellular chemistry. Exposure to this chemical can cause some people to feel tired and lethargic and when inhaled may have narcotic effects. As it is broken down in the body it eventually produces a chemical known as chloral hydrate which is used in medicine as a sedative. Severe exposure to trichloroethylene fumes can lead to heart failure (glue sniffing for instance). When heated it produces highly toxic fumes that can cause lung disease and death. Exposure even up to 200 ft away may cause dermatitis. Long-term or high exposure is thought to be a cancer risk and it may also cause suppression of the immune system, liver damage, psychological impairment, memory loss and depression. Trichloroethylene can disturb cell chemistry and the brain and nerves are particularly vulnerable because they have a high lipid content. Other symptoms of toxic exposure include digestive upsets, nausea, fatigue, dizziness and heart and liver disorders.

Protection	Impact on Environment/Wildlife
Solvents may leach into indoor air and are best avoided or at least stored outside the home. Hot showers approx 42°C or over release vaporized trichloroethane into the air. When pumped through a shower head, 80 percent of the dissolved trichloroethane is liberated from the water. **Chloroform** is also released. Levels of the two chemicals are twice as high in water from hot showers as from cold showers or hot or cold baths. When taking a shower, open a window or vent and close the bathroom door to avoid contaminating the air in the rest of the house. If you have clothing dry-cleaned, hang it in the fresh air for at least one or two days, or at least keep it out of your bedroom until it has had a chance to evaporate – hang in a wardrobe only when thoroughly aired, especially during the winter when the windows are likely to be closed. Allow continental quilts to air for at least 2 days before using them – down and other fillings tend to 'hold' the chemicals in large quantities. Keep the windows open in the car when taking dry-cleaned items home. Fat-soluble antioxidant vitamins are protective against lipid cellular damage and include vitamins A and E and lipid-soluble vitamin C (ascorbyl palmitate).	Trichloroethylene is particularly persistent in the environment and pollutes water supplies.

Substance	Sources	Hazards/Toxity
TRICHLOROETHYLENE (continued)		Trichloroethylene is included in the Environmental Protection Agency (EPA) list of 'priority pollutants' classified as hazardous to human health.
XYLENE	caulking compound dry-cleaning fluids household cleaning items nail polish paint thinners pens and markers printer's ink shoe polish (liquid)	Xylene is moderately toxic if absorbed through the skin or inhaled. Prolonged exposure may cause cough, nausea or vomiting, confusion, euphoria, headaches, tinnitus, and giddiness. Breathing high concentrations of vapour causes fatigue. Extreme exposure can be fatal.

Protection	Impact on Environment/Wildlife
Xylene vapour is extremely flammable and products containing it should not be used near naked flames or cigarettes. It is a skin irritant and contact should be avoided. Always ensure that there is adequate ventilation when products containing xylene are used indoors, and as a general precaution, avoid inhaling the fumes. Vitamin C is a general detoxifier and if xylene fumes have been inhaled it may be helpful in reducing levels of the chemical in the body. Provided you are not taking specific medications (see Chapter 7), 500 mg of vitamin C can be taken every 2 hours until the symptoms subside. For chronic exposure a doctor should always be consulted before self-treatment is attempted.	No data found, but all solvents should be used only when absolutely necessary. Because of their widespread use their disposal may pose environmental problems.

THE ALTERNATIVES

☑ Air fresheners

Air fresheners are usually marketed as aerosols and contain a vast conglomeration of chemicals, some of which may be unpleasant or dangerous if inhaled. Some products contain imidazoline, a chemical which blocks the ability to smell by affecting the nervous system.

It is preferable to open windows rather than fill the air you breathe with chemicals, but if this is impossible keep a bottle of Air Therapy handy. This product is a completely natural air freshener made from pure citrus oils which reduces airborne odours and is packed in a pump-action spray. For more details, see under Cleaning and Housekeeping in Chapter 8.

Home-made air fresheners can be very effective:

BAKING SODA acts as an effective refrigerator deodorizer – leave an open container in the fridge. Sprinkling a little baking soda into the bottom of kitchen bins will help to prevent the growth of moulds and decrease odours.

STRIKING A MATCH in the bathroom is preferable to using aerosol air sprays which are a source of numerous toxic chemicals including **formaldehyde**, propellants, chemical fragrances, **naphthalene, phenol** and **xylene**. But it is advisable to avoid breathing the match's smoke as it contains **antimony**.

In centrally heated rooms put a few EUCALYPTUS LEAVES into the water in radiator-mounted humidifiers. Placing ROSEMARY TWIGS on the fire will freshen a room in the winter.

☑ Clothes washing

Some commercial washing powders contain phosphates and these lead to disruption of aquatic life. It is preferable to use Ecover or another BIODEGRADABLE WASHING POWDER, adding approximately 4 oz of BAKING SODA to the water to help deodorize and clean clothes; this also has the advantage of making hard water a little softer and further increasing the cleaning ability of the powder.

☑ Disinfectants

Commercial disinfectants or toilet cleaners may contain **ammonia**, chlorine, **formaldehyde** and numerous unpleasant chemicals, and they are hard on the environment. Oxygen or hydrogen peroxide bleaches are a slightly safer alternative to chlorine bleaches; however, they still kill vital bacteria which act on sewage to break it down, either in septic tanks or as far down the line as sewage works.

One alternative is 1 tablespoon of BORAX dissolved in a pint of hot water. This solution has disinfectant properties. Although it is less toxic than most commercial disinfectants or bleaches, it should still be used with caution and kept away from children and the eyes. Ecover and several new companies manufacture BIODEGRADABLE TOILET CLEANERS.

☑ Drain cleaner

Before resorting to noxious and highly poisonous chemicals for a drain blockage, use a plunger. If this fails try pouring 6 oz of SALT and 6 oz of BAKING SODA down the sink followed by a pint of boiling water. Allow to sit overnight then flush with water.

Alternatively, try 4 oz of BAKING SODA and 8 oz of VINEGAR in 2 pints of boiling water. Cover and leave for a minute then rinse well, or leave overnight and rinse well with hot water in the morning.

To prevent drain blockages use a drain trap and use a mixture of 2 oz BAKING SODA, 2 oz SALT and 1 oz CREAM OF TARTAR. Pour into the drain followed by a jug of boiling water, then a jug of cold once a week to help dissolve grease and other potential blockers.

☑ Furniture polish

Furniture polishes are a witches brew of chemicals often packaged in aerosols. The natural alternatives require a little more elbow grease but will not pollute indoor air. Natural BEESWAX POLISHES are available from some health stores and are a safer alternative to silicone sprays and chemical polishes.

Alternatively, you can concoct a home-made polish from 1 part VINEGAR and 3 parts OLIVE OIL. Furniture can also be rubbed with a clean cloth dipped in cool tea and then quickly buffed dry. A more ambitious mixture can be made from 1 teaspoon of OLIVE OIL, the juice of a LEMON, 1 teaspoon of BRANDY and a teaspoon of WATER. For darker wood use a mixture of WHITE VINEGAR and WARM WATER in equal quantities. Wipe into wood then polish with a dry chamois.

☑ Hard water stains

Commercial cleaners are not necessarily toxic, but inexpensive alternatives work equally well: rub the area where limescale has built up – as a result of dripping taps for instance – with a cloth soaked in LEMON JUICE or a mixture of SALT and VINEGAR. Leave on for five minutes and rinse off.

☑ Kettle descaler

Commercial kettle descaling products (except OZ) contain **formic acid** and sulphamic acid, both of which release highly irritant fumes when heated. The chemicals may also cause stomach upset if they are not removed thoroughly after use and find their way into the drinking water.

A safe and inexpensive alternative is to immerse the kettle element in VINEGAR just beyond the minimum safe level. Bring it to the boil and allow to cool. Rinse several times then boil again. Empty the water and rinse once more.

☑ Metal cleaners

Certain metal cleaners can contain a cocktail of petroleum-based chemicals and a form of **ammonia** which is highly toxic if swallowed and should be kept away from skin and eyes. There are many alternatives to chemical cleaners, all of which are common items in the kitchen:

COPPER AND BRONZE
Clean with a mixture of SALT and LEMON JUICE or VINEGAR.

BRASS AND COPPER
For brass, a cleaner can be made from a mixture of 1 tablespoon of SALT, 2 tablespoons of FLOUR and enough water to make it into a paste. Cover the object with the paste and allow to dry, then wash off and buff with a soft cloth.

Brass and copper can be cleaned with SOUR MILK or YOGURT: coat the object, allow it to dry, then rinse off and buff with a soft cloth. Alternatively, use WORCESTER SAUCE. After cleaning brass, rub it with OLIVE OIL to increase brightness.

ALUMINIUM
Clean with LEMON JUICE on a cloth and rinse with warm water. Keep sodium carbonate (washing soda) away from aluminium as it may attack the surface of the metal.

CHROME
Clean with undiluted CIDER VINEGAR or rub with LEMON PEEL and polish with a soft cloth.

GOLD
Wash in warm SOAPY WATER, dry with a cloth and polish with a chamois.

SILVER
TOOTHPASTE can be used to clean silver which can then be polished with a chamois. Alternatively, half fill a large ceramic or glass bowl with strips of 'SILVER' FOIL. Add a tablespoon of SALT and enough cold water to fill the bowl. Dip silver items into the solution for approximately 2 minutes, then rinse.

☑ Mould cleaner

Ordinary household mould cleaners usually comprise a number of unpleasant chemicals, so before resorting to these try some natural alternatives. Use a stiff brush with BAKING SODA and enough hot water to make a paste. BORAX dissolved in hot water also removes mould.

To prevent mould growth keep the room well aired and dry. If there are no windows in the room install a full-spectrum light tube and leave on for at least 4 hours a day. It is UV light that prevents mould growth. Fluorescent FSLs use much less electricity than tungsten bulbs so it won't be expensive.

☑ Oven cleaner

Prevention is better than the chemical cure. It is helpful to cook foods in slightly larger cookware to lessen the chance of spills. Aluminium foil can be used to line the oven as long as it does not touch food, but it is a rather unecological option.

To make an effective oven cleaner for less persistent spills, make a paste from BAKING SODA and water and spread over greasy areas. Leave on for approximately three minutes then wash off with a scouring cloth and hot water. Using an abrasive cloth or powder on glass can cause it to shatter when the oven is hot; most self-cleaning ovens have a special coating which will be damaged by abrasive products.

If the grease is not too heavy and not baked on to the surface, Ecover or Clearspring washing-up liquid may be sufficient to clean the area, especially for routine cleaning. WASHING SODA dissolved in warm water can also be used (but wear gloves). Sprinkle SALT on a spill while it is still warm and it will be much easier to remove when the oven cools.

Chemical oven cleaners are among the worst indoor air polluters, and despite extremely careful rinsing some of the chemicals can remain in joints and corners and continue to release vapours when the oven is heated. If you do have to resort to a chemical cleaner it is best to wear rubber gloves to protect your hands, and this applies also when using milder chemicals: washing soda, for instance, can remove the first layer of the skin.

☑ Pests

Before reaching for the ubiquitous pest sprays, try some gentler alternatives:

ANTS dislike MINT so a few plants grown outside a doorway where they are likely to enter will deter them. They are also not enamoured of CAYENNE PEPPER or BORAX mixed 50:50 with sugar. A line of either can be placed around areas where they are likely to enter the building. *Avoid putting borax down if children or pets will have access to the area.* (If you can bring yourself to do it, a kettle of boiling water poured into ant holes will often do the trick.)

COCKROACHES are also repelled by BORAX and a light dusting around the area where cockroaches enter should be effective. Holes around skirting boards, around pipes, sinks and baths should be blocked. To make a trap, grease the inner neck of a milk bottle and put a little raw potato or stale beer into it. Cockroaches tempted into the bottle will be trapped.

FLEAS can be discouraged from making your pet their home by the addition of BREWER'S YEAST and GARLIC POWDER to the normal pet food. To each meal add 1 tablespoon of yeast and 1 teaspoon of garlic powder or 1 garlic capsule. Most dogs and cats find this a pleasant addition to the diet – the only drawback is the possible odour of garlic on the animal's breath, but this should be only temporary. Sprinkle PENNYROYAL OIL onto pets' bedding and rub some into the fur after a bath as this also repels fleas.

For FLIES use old-fashioned fly papers or scratch ORANGE PEEL with a fork and leave it around a room. People used to hang bunches of DRIED LAVENDER around a room or include it in flower arrangements to discourage flies. Another option is to keep bowls of dried lavender in each room or to use Air Therapy (for more details see under Cleaning and Housekeeping in Chapter 8). Flies are attracted to sunny windows, so close them before the sun reaches them.

MOTHS are discouraged by CEDAR CHIPS or OIL, also by LAVENDER or a mixture of ROSEMARY and MINT. Wash clothes before storing them, or place them in the sun or through the dryer on the warm cycle. Unless they are stored in a moth-proof container it is a good idea to repeat this every two or three months. These measures will kill moth larvae.

☑ Tar and oil removal

It is best to avoid using chemical products as they release volatile fumes. To remove fresh tar and oil from clothes, fabric and metal items soak a piece of cotton wool with EUCALYPTUS OIL and gently rub the soiled area. Allow eucalyptus oil to soak into fabric before washing it. Keep the oil away from plastics and perspex as it will melt them. The oil can be obtained from chemists and some health stores.

☑ Window cleaner

Commercial window cleaners contain **ammonia** which can be inhaled when using window cleaning sprays. As an alternative, add about 2 fluid ounces of WHITE WINE VINEGAR to half a pint of warm water. Pour it into a spray bottle and use as you would commercial cleaner. To avoid fluff use a sheet of newspaper as a duster; this will also produce a shine.

Creating a Healthier Home

12 million Canadian dollars were spent investigating ways to remove formaldehyde from indoor air. A NASA scientist discovered that certain houseplants clean the air very efficiently.

Early in the 1970s when NASA's Skylab space missions were in progress, air quality experiments revealed that the three crew members were exposed to over three hundred volatile organic chemicals. The resulting data set off numerous investigations into air quality in buildings and the effect of pollutants on their human occupants.

It has been known for many years that gaseous toxic substances accumulate in the air of poorly ventilated rooms and buildings. In the last twenty-five years the number of products which emit trace levels of organic chemicals has increased. Chipboard, plywood and veneers, plastics and artificial fibres, insecticides, cleaners, solvents, hair sprays and cosmetics all contribute synthetic chemicals to the atmosphere inside the home, but it is only recently that it has been recognized as an actual health hazard. The adoption of energy-saving methods and decreased ventilation in homes has aggravated the situation and increased the levels of potential health hazards.

IMPROVEMENTS YOU CAN MAKE

Plants

The Canadian National Research Council invested twelve million dollars in projects on removing formaldehyde from air in the home, but a very simple and inexpensive method has been found by a NASA scientist. Dr Wolverton conducted experiments into biotechnology and discovered that *plants* are particularly efficient at clearing chemical pollutants from the indoor environment. It turns out that quite a number of ordinary house plants are capable of removing chemicals from the air, including the ubiquitous formaldehyde and combustion gases. Several spider plants are enough to remove the chemical build-up in the average double-glazed, energy efficient home.

AIR-CLEANSING PLANTS

Dwarf banana plants
Spider plants (Chlorophytum elatum)
Golden pathos (Scindapsus aureus)
Chinese evergreens
Peace lilies
Peperomia
Mother-in-law's tongue (Sansevieria)
Nephthyus (Sungomum podophyllum)

Data based on NASA plant studies

Besides ridding the air of pernicious vapours and chemicals, plants can also improve indoor air by absorbing odours and increasing humidity through evapotranspiration. Both house plants and cut flowers discharge water and oxygen which improves air quality, and many plants add a natural scent to the room.

The process of photosynthesis which allows plants to live and grow is based on a continuous exchange of gases (carbon dioxide, water vapour and oxygen) between plant leaves and the surrounding atmosphere. This includes the taking in of chemical gases and vapours from the air which are then assimilated by the plant and neutralized in a process of biodegradation. At the same time, under light conditions, plants produce and emit oxygen, an important factor in a building occupied by several people where combustion processes are taking place and ventilation levels are low.

If you have a plant working for you in an artificially lit environment with no windows or fresh air – in an office for example – it will detoxify ambient chemicals, and will also help to increase the oxygen in the air. But be nice to it: rotate its duties with other plants and locate it in an area where it will receive natural light at least once a month. Another option is to group several plants together so that the humidity around them is increased and they stay healthier. Spider plants are ideal because they do not require bright light, but both the occupants of the room and the plants would benefit from the installation of full-spectrum light tubes in place of the regular fluorescent variety if there is no natural light (see Chapter 8).

In the future we may be using high tech plant air filtration systems combining an activated carbon filter in the plant soil with an air pump. This has been tested and shows the potential to remove relatively large quantities of chemicals and smoke from indoor air. Biotechnology has other promising applications too, including removing hazardous chemicals from drinking, ground and river water, removing toxic chemicals from industrial wastewaters, and removing radioactive waste and other hazardous chemicals from contaminated soil and water.

Negative Ions

Air that is overcharged with positive ions has a negative effect on health, and air balanced with negative ions has a positive effect on health. Our homes and workplaces often generate and trap too many positive ions resulting in some (but not all) of the occupants complaining of fatigue, irritability, tension, anxiety, depression or unnatural tiredness. Many common household items generate positive ions in the air – these include electric bar and fan heaters made with nickel chromium wire elements, electrical equipment, synthetic fabrics, TV and VDU screens and synthetic wall-to-wall carpets. Heating and air-conditioning systems deplete negative ions and add positive ions to the air during recirculation through metal ducts.

The nervous system functions by minute electrical impulses based on ion exchange and because of this it can be sensitive to electrical alterations in the atmosphere. A recognizable example of this occurs before and after thunderstorms. Before a storm the air becomes heavy with positive ions and after a storm the lightning and rain will have produced high levels of negative ions. Even if you are not physically affected by the change, it is noticeable that the air feels fresher and cleaner after the storm and 'heavy' before it. In some parts of the world certain desert winds occasionally carry an extreme number of positive ions and they are famous for their unpleasant effects on people. Suicide rates rise sharply when these winds blow. The Scirocco, a hot, humid south or southeast wind of south Italy, Sicily and the Mediterranean islands is one such wind. It originates in the Sahara desert and feels very oppressive.

In nature, negative ions are manufactured by rain, lightning, sunshine, air currents, and the breaking up of water droplets in surf, rain, waterfalls and fountains, but they have a short life span and have to be manufactured constantly. In the home the best way to increase the negative ions is to invest in an ionizer (see Chapter 8). These simple machines release thousands of negatively charged ions into the air every second, cleaning positively charged dust, smoke and airborne pollutants by attracting and negatively charging them. This effectively makes them heavier so that they sink rather than float in the air where they will be breathed in.

The torch cactus (*Cereus peruvianus*), column-like in appearance, can be used as a low tech alternative to an ionizer to counteract the fatigue and headaches sometimes experienced by people who work long hours in front of a VDU or are exposed to electronic equipment at close range. This discovery is being utilized by workers on the New York Stock Exchange to restore equilibrium to the electromagnetically disturbed environment and has equal potential in any area where electronic equipment is being used.

Rebalancing the air offers numerous benefits, especially during the winter months or in workplaces where windows are rarely opened. A high level of negative ions increases the body's capacity to absorb oxygen. People who live or work with smokers, especially those who find wearing contact lenses uncomfortable due to smoke irritation, benefit from an ionizer's ability to decrease smoke levels in the air. Using an ionizer can also help to reduce airborne infections because bacteria travel in the air attached to dust particles.

Colour

Colour is very important in our lives. Emotionally, colours are associated with feelings: 'being off-colour', 'black as thunder', 'feeling blue' and 'seeing red'. It has both subconscious effects and a direct effect on the nervous system. Colour is part of the electromagnetic spectrum which also includes cosmic rays, gamma rays, X-rays, ultraviolet rays, infrared rays, and radio and television rays. Every colour vibrates at a different level, therefore causing different degrees of density in the atmosphere around us. Red resonates at 4.6 trillion vibrations per second; it is the most dense colour. Blue vibrates 7.5 trillion times a second and is the least dense. All the other colours fall somewhere in between.

Light enters the eye and is transmitted via the optic nerve to the hypothalamus in the brain. The hypothalamus controls the pituitary gland, part of the autonomic nervous system which controls functions like the heart rate and digestive system. This may explain why sitting in a red room (red is a stimulating colour) can increase appetite and activity and even raise blood pressure. Several colour experiments have been carried out using sighted and blind volunteers, and the corresponding biological results suggest that vibrations from the light also affect the body and mind of a blind person.

In the home, room colours can have a positive or negative effect on the occupants; for example, royal blue is not recommended for a sitting room as it can cut conversation, whereas shades of blue are helpful for poor sleepers. Colours have also been utilized commercially to sell us products, and an airline which changed its interior decor from yellow and brown to blue found that airsickness decreased by almost half.

The natural pigments taken from plants, minerals and resin oils used in natural paints and varnishes (see LIVOS and AURO in Chapter 8) are more earthy and less vibrant than their chemical counterparts, and the hues are more in harmony with a natural environment. When planning room colours allow the following points to have a bearing on your choices:

Chart 3.1 Effects of colour on mood

Colour	Reported Biological Effects
Red	A heating, revitalizing and stimulating colour often used in public places to stimulate conversation, for example. People who live on their nerves or are bad sleepers often find that painting rooms in their home red increases their activity or excitability and affects their sleep adversely.
Blue	The opposite to red. It is calm, cooling and emotionally sedative. Blue hues encourage relaxation and a blue window shade or blue curtains have been found to promote daytime relaxation. Also helpful for nightworkers who have to sleep during daylight hours.
Yellow	A cheering colour also connected with the intellect. It is linked to the left side of the brain and may help concentration and boost learning ability. It is a good colour for an office or a homework or study area.
Green	The colour of harmony and balance. It is also a healing and quieting colour at the cooler end of the spectrum. Both blues and greens are often suggested for bedrooms.
Pink	Pink tones are related to red and for some people can be mentally draining. It is considered to be the colour of universal healing, with a potential for raising the vibrations of the body.
Turquoise	Can be tranquillizing, cooling and relaxing.
White	White is neutral and contains all the colours of the spectrum.

Although bright colours are generally considered to be stimulating and cooler colours relaxing, studies have revealed that some hyperactive children tend to become calmer in rooms with bright colours and slow-learning children may be stimulated by cool colours. Since each child is different it may be worth watching them in different coloured environments and drawing your own conclusions, possibly utilizing the information to colour the child's room.

Full-Spectrum Light

Sunlight is a combination of all colours of the spectrum, whereas artificial light contains only certain wavelengths. Dr John Ott and other light researchers have found that depriving the body and brain of full-spectrum light can produce illness, or at least lead to mild forms of ill health, especially when exposure to natural sunlight is extremely limited.

Life on earth is influenced by the sun, moon, gravity, and the earth's rotation around the sun. Light is a powerful force and its effects on our psyche and many processes, including glandular function, are very important. As full-spectrum light (and colour) passes through the eye it is directed first to the hypothalamus in the brain, which regulates the glands, reproduction, sleep and waking, appetite, and body temperature, and to the pineal gland in the brain, which stops its production of a mood-depressing and sleep-inducing hormone called melatonin. People who suffer from the medically recognized winter blues syndrome known as seasonal affective disorder or SAD are showing advanced symptoms of full-spectrum light deprivation. In order to reverse oversleeping, lethargy, craving for carbohydrates, overeating, weight gain, loss of interest in work, social and sexual activity and other symptoms, SAD victims spend a few hours a day exposed to light boxes comprising several fluorescent bulbs which mimic the spectrum of natural daylight. This decreases melatonin levels, stimulates the hypothalamus and allows them to function normally over the darkest months of the year.

Ordinary glass prevents up to ninety-nine percent of UV light entering a building, or the eyes if glass-lensed glasses are worn. If you spend most of your time indoors during the winter it would be worth investigating the installation of full-spectrum lights (see Chapter 8 for more details). Working or living under full-spectrum lights in the winter can have a positive effect on mood, health, work efficiency and alertness. Indoor light quality is an important part of a healthy indoor environment.

HAZARDS TO AVOID

Plant Dangers

The leaves of tomatoes, potatoes and rhubarb are well known for their toxicity, and many garden and house plant leaves, seeds, berries or bulbs can also be poisonous if eaten. Children are especially vulnerable because they have a smaller volume of blood than adults and ingested poisons are therefore less diluted. How much of a plant can be eaten before it has toxic effects depends upon how poisonous it is – and the strength of the poison can fluctuate according to the age of the plant, the time of year and the weather. Because of this the information in the following chart should be considered only as a general guide; also, it is not possible to compile a complete list. To be safe teach children not to eat *any* berries or leaves, and keep very young children away from them. Packet seeds can also be toxic and should be kept away from children.

Chart 3.2 Plants which are poisonous if eaten

House/Garden Plant	Possible Danger If Ingested
Amaryllis	Nausea, vomiting, diarrhoea and abdominal cramps.
Anthurium	Stomach upset and breathing difficulties.
Autumn Crocus	The whole of this plant is poisonous.
Azalea	Keep children/animals away, poisonous.
Black Bryony	The red autumn berries are poisonous and cause burning of the mouth as a warning.
Boston Ivy	Stomach upset and breathing difficulties.
Buttercup	Nausea, vomiting, diarrhoea and abdominal cramps.

Calla Lily	Stomach upset and breathing difficulties.
Carnation	Nausea, vomiting, diarrhoea and abdominal cramps.
Conkers (from the horse chestnut tree)	May be mistaken for chestnuts and can cause stomach upsets and vomiting.
Cuckoopint	The orange/red berries are extremely poisonous but burn the mouth as a warning.
Daffodil	Nausea, vomiting, diarrhoea and abdominal cramps.
Daisy	Nausea, vomiting, diarrhoea and abdominal cramps.
Deadly and Black Nightshades	The berries are highly poisonous.
Dieffenbachia	The sap from the leaves may irritate the mouth and throat if eaten. Wash hands after touching the plant and keep them away from the eyes.
Elder	Raw berries can cause stomach pains, vomiting and diarrhoea.
Ficus Benjamina	Nausea, vomiting, diarrhoea and abdominal cramps.
Foxglove	The entire plant is poisonous including the flowers.
Geranium	Nausea, vomiting, diarrhoea and abdominal cramps.
Hogweed, Giant	The sap can cause painful skin blisters.
Hemlock	The leaves and roots are extremely toxic. Ingestion has been known to prove fatal.
Holly berries	Nausea, vomiting, diarrhoea and abdominal cramps.
Hydrangea	Can be poisonous to children and animals.

Laburnum	The green seedpods can cause burning of the mouth, stomach upsets and dizziness.
Lily of the valley	The berries may make a child so sick that the toxicants are ejected before they cause poisoning.
Lupin	Seeds and the seedpods are poisonous: two seedpods may be enough to cause headache and nausea or vomiting.
Mistletoe berries	Digestive upsets and abdominal cramps.
Monkshood	An extremely poisonous plant – professional help should be sought as soon as possible if eaten.
Oleander	All parts of this plant are poisonous.
Philodendron	Stomach upset and breathing difficulties.
Privet	The small black berries which appear after flowering can make a child ill. Keep privet hedges clipped regularly to avoid flowering if children will be playing in the garden.
Tulip, daffodil and crocus bulbs	Nausea, vomiting, diarrhoea and stomach cramps.
Yew	The berry seeds can be lethally poisonous if chewed and swallowed.

IN AN EMERGENCY . . .

If a child has eaten a poisonous plant or berry the **mouth or throat may be irritated and/or swollen**; the more severe symptoms such as **feeling sick with diarrhoea or stomach pains** may develop within about forty-eight hours of ingesting a poisonous plant.

If the mouth or throat is irritated, flush with cool water and take the child to a doctor or the casualty department. If possible, take a sample of the plant or leaf with you. If the child vomits, keep a sample for the doctor but do not try to induce vomiting, even if the child complains of feeling sick with diarrhoea or stomach pains. Inducing vomiting or providing a drink may speed the poison into the bloodstream.

Children are rarely very seriously ill from eating poisonous plants or berries. If it is suggested that the child stays in hospital overnight for observation, this is often just a routine safety precaution.

Chemical Cocktails

Mixing certain household and DIY items together can result in the production of dangerous toxic vapours or compounds. The list which follows is a guide to some of the products which should always be kept apart.

Chart 3.3 Chemicals which should never be combined

Product/Chemical	Mixed With	Result/Danger
Ammonia	Oven cleaners (sodium hydroxide, caustic soda, lye)	Release of highly toxic ammonia gas
	Dodecyclamine fungicide and mould inhibitor	As above
Ammonium Sulphate and Ammonium Persulphate	Flammable products chemicals	Explosion or fire
Bleach (including sodium hyperchlorite oxygen bleaches)	Toilet cleaners containing acid including vinegar	A highly toxic chlorine gas will be produced
	Powdered toilet cleaners containing	As above

Bleach (continued)	sodium hydrogen sulphate	
	Wood filler containing styrene	Production of powerfully irritating vapours
	Ammonia	Production of toxic chloramine fumes
Mercoprop Herbicide Lawn Products	Dicambra Dichlorprop herbicide lawn products	Potentiation of each chemical's eye and skin irritant properties
Sodium Chlorate weedkiller	Acids	Explosion or fire
	Ammonium nitrate	Fire

Burning and Heating

Burning foams, plastics, synthetic carpets and fabrics, chemicals and aerosols are an extreme health hazard. If most plastic, foam and chemical items are gradually replaced in the home by more natural materials the dangers related to the burning of these items can be reduced, but the most important safety factor is the installation of fire alarms in the home. Choking black smoke from synthetic items contains chemicals which make breathing difficult and attack the bloodstream: carbon monoxide, phosgene gas (used in chemical warfare), hydrogen cyanide, toluene, dioxins and ammonia. Once inhaled, these chemicals make it difficult to function normally and are responsible for more fatalities than the actual fires.

Burning synthetic or chemical-based items on a bonfire or in the home grate can seriously endanger health, and the accidental or innocent heating or burning of some items can result in the release of life-threatening vapours, gases or fumes. Never heat or burn the following:

Chart 3.4 Substances which are extremely dangerous when burned

Item or Chemical	Hazards
Ammonium nitrate (artificial fertilizer)	When heated may explode; releases highly toxic fumes
Arsenic trioxide (found in some yacht anti-fouling paints)	Heating produces toxic arsenic fumes
Fenoprop (lawn weedkiller)	Heating produces toxic fumes
4-indol-3-ylbutryric acid (herbicide used in some rooting powders)	Heating produces toxic fumes
Maleic hydrazide (tree and shrub growth regulator)	Heating produces toxic fumes
Parachlorometacresol (yacht anti-fouling agent and masonry biocide)	Releases highly toxic phosgene gas when heated
Phenols (found in creosote and other wood preservatives)	Release toxic fumes when heated
Phenothrin (insecticide)	Releases acrid fumes when heated
Plastics containing nitrogen (polyurethane, acrylic, melamine)	Release highly toxic hydrogen cyanide gas
Polyurethane foam	Releases highly toxic hydrogen cyanide gas
Polyvinyl chloride (PVC)	Releases dioxin, phosgene and hydrogen chloride when burned
Thiram (yacht anti-fouling agent and fungicide)	When burned releases poisonous gases

1,1,1-Trichloroethane (solvent used in correction fluids, suede and leather protection sprays, some adhesives, stain removers)	If partially burned this solvent releases highly toxic phosgene gas
Toluene (solvent used in damp treatments, glues, cleaning products, polyurethane, paint thinners, stain removers, nail polish)	Highly irritant toluene fumes are released from burning items containing this solvent
Trichloroethylene (solvent used in leather guard agents, degreasers, fragrances, DIY and household items, paints, stain removers and some pesticides as an 'inert' ingredient	Toxic fumes are produced when items containing this chemical are heated or burned
Wood treated with Lindane	Releases highly toxic phosgene gas when burned

HEALTHY HOME CHECKLIST

✘ Burning colour newspapers or magazines in the fireplace liberates lead from the inks into the air. This is particularly dangerous for children especially if the room is badly ventilated. Burning plastics releases toluene which is highly toxic when inhaled.

✔ Store medicines in a locked cabinet if children will be in the home and make sure all poisonous substances are well out of the reach of children, preferably keeping all chemicals in a locked cupboard. Keep chemicals in their original containers rather than transferring them to bottles or jars where they may be mistaken for food or drink. Never leave paintbrushes soaking in turps as children may play with it or drink it.

✔ Buy plain wallpaper paste without mould-inhibiting chemicals and mix a little borax with it to inhibit moulds without the prospect of chemicals being released into the atmosphere.

✔ Use photoelectric smoke detectors rather than those which contain radioactive americium-241. (See **radiation** in Chapter 2 and Chapter 6.)

✘ Mixing different household cleaners, bleaches and chemicals together can produce powerfully toxic vapours.

✔ Save painting jobs and DIY which involves the use of chemicals until the summer when the home can be well ventilated. Sleep in a newly decorated bedroom only after 6 to 10 days have elapsed, or when the odour has decreased. Circulating air dries paint more rapidly than heat. Preferably use organic paints and DIY products. (See Chapter 8 for more information.)

✔ If you cook with a gas oven or gas burners, ventilate the room well and if possible use an extractor fan to remove nitrogen dioxide, carbon monoxide and formaldehyde from the room. If the flame on your gas range burns orange instead of blue ask the gas board to adjust it for you.

✓ Gas appliances should be fitted by an installer registered with the Confederation for the Registration of Gas Installers (CORGI) and regular servicing should be carried out. Inspect chimneys and flues for cracks and leaks.

✓ When taking a hot shower (42°C or more) close the bathroom door and vent the steam outside the home. Hot showers release vaporized trichloroethylene and chloroform into the air. Up to 50 percent of the dissolved chloroform and 80 percent of the trichloroethylene are liberated by heating and passing water through a shower head. The release of chemicals is half that amount with cold showers or hot baths.

✓ If you have clothing dry-cleaned, hang it in the fresh air for at least 1 to 2 days, or at least keep it out of your bedroom until the solvent chemicals have had a chance to evaporate. Hang the clothes in a wardrobe only when thoroughly aired, especially during the winter when the windows are likely to be closed. Allow continental quilts to air for at least 2 days before using them. Down and other fillings tend to 'hold' volatile chemicals in large quantities. Keep the windows open in the car when taking dry-cleaned items home.

✓ Keep wall and ceiling ventilators in kitchens and bathrooms open. They are designed to vent gases from boilers, waterheaters and other appliances.

✓ Ensure good ventilation if using gas or paraffin space heaters.

✓ Store aerosols and non-biodegradable cleaning products high up on a shelf in a garden shed or a very well ventilated area; when stored under a sink they can release toxic vapours into the air. Aerosols should never be exposed to heat; if exposed to extreme heat they are liable to explode. It is best to avoid aerosols completely.

✔Begin to phase out chemical products by finding safer alternatives. The same applies to garden chemicals – any you are still using should be stored in a sealed and marked box high up on a shelf in a garage or shed.

✔Put spider plants in each room to clean formaldehyde and other chemicals from indoor air.

Chemical-Free Gardening

'Each year 20 million pounds are spent on garden chemicals. If every gardener stopped using pesticides, it would create a conservation area of over one million acres.'

Henry Doubleday Research Association

THE CASE AGAINST CHEMICALS

Nearly fifty years ago, when chemicals were first considered as a breakthrough in agricultural production, no one was able to foresee the problems that their extensive use would create. DDT was the first major chemical adapted for use as a pesticide, and at the time its extraordinary persistence in soil, its infiltration of the food chain and the dangers to wildlife were not envisaged. These repercussions became obvious only when the damage had already been done.

Chemicals are still a major component of agriculture, and the home gardener, too, has been persuaded by powerful advertising and an induced fear of all things creeping to resort to an armament of chemicals the instant an insect ventures into the garden. But even with the huge array of chemicals, including broad-spectrum insecticides (a euphemism for the fact that they kill everything they come into contact with), pests continue to survive and thrive. In fact, you can bombard the garden to choking point with potent concoctions only to find that the minute your back is turned hordes of insects scale the garden fence and start a residents' committee in your petunias or your prize vegetables. The reason, according to organic gardening experts, is that the vacuum left by the effects of chemicals has to be filled, and the insects most likely to perform the service are the more exasperating hardy varieties. This is partly because their natural predators succumb to the chemical assault along with the pests. Furthermore, chemicals kill soil microbes, which leads to the gradual weakening of the soil and creates weaker, insect-attracting plants.

> Insects are nature's way of destroying inferior vegetation as they prefer to feed on plants with chemical imbalances or those that are mildly diseased.

Chemicals not only upset the ecological balance in the soil, but they can also pose dangers while being stored – they may be ingested by mistake, and there are also dangers associated with handling them. There is a huge number of chemicals available to the householder and there may be considerable deficiencies in the safety data on them. Numerous popular chemicals have been in use for years and have not been tested to the current, more stringent safety standards; others like 2,4,5-T are banned in several countries, but are freely available to British gardeners. When some of the older chemicals were retested in the late 1980s it resulted in the withdrawal of a number of them, including the popular lawn treatment inoxynil. Other worries centre around the fact that, firstly, there have been no assessments of the health risks associated with the reactions between different chemicals, and secondly, disposing of them creates a further environmental hazard.

> Unwanted insecticides and other garden chemicals do not 'disappear' when tipped down a drain. Sewage treatment works cannot remove these chemicals, only dilute them.

Effects on Humans

Chemicals used on an agricultural scale obviously have the potential to cause the most damage, both to soil and to the environment, but given the scale of domestic horticulture and the huge sums of money spent on garden chemicals, it is important to remember that the potential for environmental damage exists also in the garden. The following chart lists some of the chemicals are widely available and their hazards or toxicity to humans and domestic pets. Their effects on wildlife and the soil are identified in Chart 4.3.

Chart 4.1 Toxic effects of common gardening chemicals

Synthetic Chemical	Function	Hazards/Toxicity
Ammonium sulphamate	Weedkiller	Moderately poisonous if swallowed; skin and respiratory irritant.
Ammonium sulphate	Mosskiller	Moderately poisonous if swallowed.
Atrazine	Weedkiller	Moderately poisonous; if swallowed may have cumulative effects. It is an eye and skin irritant and can cause allergic reactions. Atrazine is listed on the EC chemical 'Black List' and the Government's 'Red List' of chemicals considered to be so toxic, persistent or bio-accumulative in the environment that steps should be taken to eliminate pollution by them.
Benazolin	Weedkiller/ growth regulator	Mild eye and skin irritant.
Benomyl	Fungicide	Slightly poisonous if swallowed. The USEPA has classified this chemical as a possible human carcinogen and it has caused birth defects and reduced sperm count in laboratory animals.

Synthetic Chemical	Function	Hazards/Toxicity
Carbaryl	Insecticide	Poisonous if swallowed and if absorbed through the skin. It is an eye and skin irritant. Particularly toxic to dogs. It is a suspected cancer-causing agent and has been linked with birth defects.
Carbendazim	Fungicide, wood preservative	Should be kept away from skin and eyes and not used in confined or badly ventilated areas. Keep pets and children away while drying.
Chlordane	Pesticide	Illegal for amateur use since 1988. If this chemical is still in your possession contact your local environmental health department for advice on how to dispose of it safely. Chlordane is very poisonous if swallowed and can be absorbed through the skin. It is a possible human cancer-causing agent and has been linked with birth defects. It is an eye and skin irritant. Like DDT, it accumulates in fatty tissue in the body and its toxic effects may take many years to become apparent.
Chlorpyrifos	Insecticide	Eye and skin irritant; poisonous if swallowed. It is an anticholinesterase agent. *
Copper sulphate	Fungicide	High or frequent exposure may affect the eyes, skin and lungs.

Synthetic Chemical	Function	Hazards/Toxicity
Creosote	Wood preservative	Contains high quantities of phenols and is carcinogenic. It is highly poisonous if swallowed, inhaled or absorbed through the skin. Keep animals and children away while creosote dries and keep it from contaminating soil. Protect the skin and eyes. Keep it away from fish ponds. For more detailed information see Data Sheets in Chapter 2.
Cypermethrin	Wood preservative, insecticide	Protect the eyes and avoid breathing the vapour; skin contact may produce irritation. For more information see Data Sheets in Chapter 2.
2,4-D	Lawn treatments, herbicide	Protect skin and eyes. This chemical was a component of Agent Orange used in the Vietnam war and, like 2,4,5-T, contains traces of dioxin. A study commissioned by the US National Cancer Institute linked 2,4-D with lymphatic cancer in rare cases where exposure was high. In animal tests it is carcinogenic and teratogenic. Skin exposure has resulted in acute, delayed nervous system damage in humans, and other effects include irritation to the throat and respiratory tract. Avoid products containing this chemical.

Synthetic Chemical	Function	Hazards/Toxicity
Dalapon	Weedkiller	Protect the skin and eyes. Moderately poisonous if swallowed.
Demeton-s-methyl	Insecticide	Highly poisonous if swallowed and is an anticholinesterase agent.*
Diazinon	Insecticide	Can be fatal if swallowed. Irritant to skin and eyes and easily absorbed through the skin. It is an anticholinesterase agent*. There is evidence that this chemical could cause birth defects and high exposure is also linked with muscle twitches, blurred vision, headaches, dizziness, flu-like symptoms and tightness in the chest.
Dicamba	Herbicide	Skin and eye irritant which is moderately poisonous if swallowed.
Dichlorophen	Lawn treatments, fungi and mould treatments	Protect the skin and eyes; may cause contact dermatitis. Moderately poisonous if swallowed. If using indoors ensure that there is adequate ventilation.
Dichlorprop	Herbicide, lawn treatments	Irritant to eyes, skin and respiratory system and moderately poisonous if swallowed or absorbed through the skin.

Synthetic Chemical	Function	Hazards/Toxicity
Dieldrin	Wood preservative	Totally banned since 1989. Highly poisonous and damaging to the environment. It is 40 times more toxic than DDT if absorbed through the skin. See Data Sheets in Chapter 2 for more details.
Dimethoate	Insecticide; found particularly in aphid sprays	Very poisonous by all routes of ingestion and is an anticholinesterase agent. * Preferably avoid its use on edible crops or leave at least a week before picking.
Dinocap	Fungicide	Irritant to eyes, skin and respiratory system, may cause contact dermatitis. Avoid contaminating edible crops.
Diquat	Weedkiller	May be fatal through all routes of ingestion including skin absorption, and there is no known antidote. May cause severe eye and skin irritation. It is best to avoid contaminating food crops with this chemical as there is disagreement about a safe period of time between treating and eating.
Diuron	Weedkiller	Irritating to eyes, skin and respiratory system; moderately poisonous if swallowed. Keep away from pets and children.
Dodecylamine	Fungicide/ mould inhibitor	Keep away from eyes and skin.

Synthetic Chemical	Function	Hazards/Toxicity
Fenitrothion	Insecticide	Very poisonous if swallowed, less if absorbed through the skin. It is an anticholinesterase agent*. This chemical appears on the EC chemical 'Black List' and the Government's 'Red List'.
Fenoprop	Lawn treatments, weedkiller	Irritant to eyes, skin and respiratory tract and moderately poisonous if swallowed.
Glyphosate	Weedkiller	Potent eye and skin irritant, slightly poisonous if swallowed.
HCH (Lindane)	Insecticide, woodworm treatment	See Data Sheets in Chapter 2.
Heptenophos	Insecticide	Anticholinesterase agent;* highly poisonous if swallowed.
Ioxynil	Lawn treatments	Withdrawn in 1988 due to its toxicity.
Malathion	Aphid sprays	Very poisonous if swallowed. It is an anticholinesterase agent* and is irritant to the eyes and skin. This chemical appears on the EC 'Black List' and the Government's 'Red List'.
Mancozeb	Fungicide	Irritating to skin, eyes and respiratory tract and is slightly poisonous if swallowed.

Synthetic Chemical	Function	Hazards/Toxicity
MCPA	Lawn treatments, herbicide	Poisonous if inhaled or absorbed through the skin. Moderately poisonous if swallowed. Keep away from eyes and skin. Avoid putting treated grass clippings in the compost as the chemical is persistent.
Mecoprop	Lawn treatments, herbicide	Poisonous through all routes of ingestion. Protect skin and eyes. Mecoprop is a suspected mutagen.
Metaldehyde	Slug pellets	May be fatal to children or animals if swallowed. Block off area to be treated and remove dead slugs or snails as birds feeding on them may be poisoned.
Methiocarb	Slug pellets	Very poisonous if swallowed. Block off area to be treated and remove dead slugs or snails as birds feeding on them may be poisoned. Keep children and animals away. This chemical is an anticholinesterase agent.*
Paraquat	Weedkiller	May be fatal if swallowed and there is no known antidote. Protect skin and eyes. Marijuana contaminated with paraquat caused deaths in the USA in the early 1980s. It has been linked with cases of aplastic anaemia (see glossary).

Synthetic Chemical	Function	Hazards/Toxicity
Paraquat (continued)		Keep children and animals away from treated area. Preferably, do not use this chemical.
Pyrethroids	Insecticides	See Data Sheets in Chapter 2.
Pirimicarb	Insecticide, aphid sprays	Avoid aerosol formulas especially if they contain anticholinesterase agents.* See later in this chapter for safer alternative aphid treatments.
Pirimiphos-methyl	Insecticide	May be irritating to eyes and skin and is moderately toxic if swallowed. An anticholinesterase agent.*
Propachlor	Weedkiller	If ingested it may accumulate in the body and is poisonous if swallowed. It is considered a hazard to pregnant women.
Propiconazole	Fungicide	Keep away from skin and eyes.
Propoxur	Insecticide	This chemical is an anticholinesterase agent,* poisonous if swallowed. It is irritating to skin or eyes.
Pyrazophos	Fungicide	Anticholinesterase agent* which is highly poisonous if swallowed.
Pyrethroids	Insecticide	See Data Sheets in Chapter 2.
Simazine	Weedkiller	Keep clear of skin and eyes. This chemical is used by

Synthetic Chemical	Function	Hazards/Toxicity
Simazine (continued)		councils etc. for keeping weeds down on pavements and paths. Its main drawback is that it contaminates water environments including drinking water. It appears on the Government's 'Red List' of toxic and persistent chemicals.
2,3,6-TBA	Herbicide	Poisonous if swallowed and may contain nitrosamines (see glossary). Keep away from skin, eyes and mucous membranes.
2,4,5-T	Brushkiller	Extremely poisonous and persistent in soil. Banned in over ten countries and outlawed by numerous British councils and British Rail. 2,4,5-T is available to gardeners in a product called Kilnet and should be avoided completely. 2,4,5-T is the controversial defoliant Agent Orange used in the Vietnam war.
Thiophanate-methyl	Fungicide	Poisonous if swallowed. One of the breakdown products in the body is cancer-causing and causes cell alteration or mutation; it can also cause birth defects.
Tributyltin Oxide (TBTO)	Wood preservative, masonry biocide	See Data Sheets in Chapter 2 for details.

Synthetic Chemical	Function	Hazards/Toxicity
Trichlorphon	Insecticide	Anticholinesterase agent* which is very irritating to the eyes. It is highly poisonous if inhaled or swallowed. Long-term exposure may cause damage to the nervous system.
Triclopyr	Herbicide	Keep away from the skin and eyes.

* Anticholinesterase agent – a substance which inhibits the action of an enzyme (cholinesterase) necessary for sending signals to the brain and causes symptoms like fainting, twitching, and impairment to reflexes and speech.

A number of wood preservatives are listed in Chapter 2 as they may be used to treat roof and other housing timbers and may therefore affect *indoor* air quality.

EMERGENCY MEASURES

Chart 4.2 Emergency measures to take in the event of poisoning

Chemical Exposure	First Aid
Poisoning	If vomiting has occurred it is important to save a sample for the doctor, but vomiting should never be induced. The mouth should be washed out with water. Telephone for a doctor or dial 999. Discover what has been swallowed if possible and provide reassurance for the person. If not breathing, clean the mouth to remove poison and give mouth to mouth resuscitation.
Skin Contamination/ Chemical Burn	Flood the affected area with water for 10 minutes and dial 999 for an ambulance. Remove clothing in the affected area unless it has adhered to the wound, and take jewellery off in case swelling occurs. Ointments, grease or butter must not be applied, but a dressing of sterile gauze or a clean cloth should be used to protect the area. As with shock, the person should be kept warm. Turn the head to one side and if the legs are not injured raise them slightly.
Eye contamination	Flood the area with clean water for 10 minutes or put the affected side of the face into a bowl of water so the eye is bathed. Telephone a doctor or dial 999. If the eye is in spasm, flood it well, open the lids with your fingers and flood again. Cover with a gauze pad and take the person to a hospital.

Chart 4.3 Effects of gardening chemicals on wildlife and soil

Toxic to: Active ingredient	Birds	Wildlife	Fish	Bees	Earthworms	Builds up in soil
Atrazine	✓		✓			
Benazolin			✓			
Benomyl		✓	✓		✓	✓
Carbaryl			✓	✓	✓	
Carbendazim			✓			✓
Chlorpyrifos	✓	✓	✓	✓		
Copper sulphate		✓	✓	✓		
Creosote			✓			
Cypermethrin			✓	✓		
Demeton-s-methyl	✓	✓	✓	✓		
Diazinon	✓	✓	✓	✓		
Dicamba			✓			
Dichlorprop		✓	✓			
Dimethoate	✓	✓	✓	✓		
Dinocap			✓			
Diquat		✓				✓
Diuron						✓
Fenitrothion	✓	✓	✓	✓		
Glyphosate			✓			
Malathion			✓	✓		✓
Mancozeb			✓			✓
MCPA	✓	✓				✓
Metaldehyde	✓		✓			
Methiocarb	✓		✓			
Paraquat	✓	✓	✓			
Pirimicarb		✓				
Pirimiphos-methyl			✓	✓		✓
Propiconazole			✓	✓		
Propoxur		✓	✓	✓		
Pyrazophos	✓	✓	✓	✓		
Simazine			✓		✓	
2,3,6-TBA			✓			
Trichlorphon			✓	✓		
Triclopyr			✓			

Effects on the Environment

Numerous chemicals have the potential to remain active for a considerable time in soil. DDT is no longer in use but is still present in the food chain, in human and animal tissue and in the soil. It is known to remain in an active state for up to forty years. This kind of persistence means that future crops and wildlife will continue to be contaminated with this and other chemicals considered to be extremely dangerous. The same happens on a diminutive scale with garden chemicals, some of which can build up in soil and contaminate food crops grown at a later date.

Bees and beneficial insects such as ladybirds and lacewing flies are killed along with the pests whenever insecticides are sprayed, and earthworms, part of the life of the soil, are killed by acids in artificial fertilizers and chemicals which migrate into the soil from sprays and other treatments. Using chemicals will inevitably upset the ecological balance and have a negative effect on the presence of birds, bees and predatory insects in your garden.

GROWING GREENER

Chemical companies spend vast sums of money persuading us that gardening without their products is impractical and unrewarding. Nothing could be further from the truth. Gardening without resorting to chemical concoctions is safer, works with, not against, the environment and builds healthier plants which naturally discourage epidemic attacks from pests by using their own defences.

One of the paradoxes of chemical agriculture is that more insecticides are needed as more chemical fertilizers are used.

Now that chemicals are such a firmly established part of domestic gardening, a paradox has developed – one which appears to support the use of chemicals. The more chemicals are used, the more they are needed, and consequently attempts at converting to organic gardening often result in a spectacular failure the first year. This convinces gardeners that chemicals are after all a necessary evil and so they go back to using them. Practically every garden has been treated with some kind of chemical, whether it is slug pellets or sprays for black and greenfly, and once treated, the vicious cycle is set up, necessitating the use of a similar treatment the next year because of the loss of natural predators and slight weakening of the plants.

One essential ingredient in converting to chemical-free gardening is perseverance, and another is remembering that 'going back to nature' is not going to happen without its hiccups. Let's face it, there are a million insect species, some 22,500 of which live in the British Isles. Also, nature has a tendency to become somewhat rampant and needs an experienced hand to tame it. Furthermore, depending on the level of chemicals formerly used, it can take from three to five years to establish basic pest immunity. But all these difficulties can be overcome.

> The first year of establishing a chemical-free garden can be disappointing, with plants that are weak and seriously attacked by pests. This is due not to a lack of chemicals, but to former chemical use and poor soil.

THE SOIL

> The secret to growing healthy crops is to feed the soil, rather than the plants.

The first step in establishing healthy pest-resistant plants is the soil. It should contain a vast array of life, from earthworms to invisible microscopic plants and bacteria. 500 billion bacteria weigh about a pound and each half acre of organic topsoil can contain from fifteen to twenty pounds. Bacteria thrive in organically rich matter and secrete substances that destroy soilborne diseases, and other microbes generate sulphuric and carbonic acids which decay rocks and release their mineral content. There is a delicate interchange between soil microorganisms and plants.

Worms increase fertility by digesting the soil and conditioning it. Their burrowing, which can reach as much as six feet down into the earth, encourages aeration, allows rain to penetrate and breaks up hard soil. Organic manure and humus are a source of food for worms, but agricultural and garden chemicals produce a chain reaction which destroys them and the other soil organisms.

> The highly acidic nature of artificial nitrate fertilizers is fatal to earthworms.

Plants take in inorganic elements from the soil and use sunlight to produce chlorophyll from which they derive their chemical energy. Water and carbon dioxide are combined to produce sugars which feed the living matter of the plant, and when the plant dies it returns it to the soil in the form of organic matter, a process which bacteria and fungi contribute to in a complex recycling process. Healthy plants in healthy soil are able to extract the correct balance of minerals from the soil to maintain their growth. Different plants have slightly different mineral requirements; so when returned to the soil through the action of microorganisms, this organic matter provides a ready supply of the nutrients needed for another cycle of growth.

The bacteria and fungi essential for the recycling process need air to thrive. Good soil aeration also ensures circulation of nitrogen and oxygen; in the process of soil respiration, oxygen is fed to plant roots producing a healthy root system and higher yields. Aeration also aids in the breakdown of organic matter. In air-poor soil, therefore, fewer minerals are available to the plants and carbon dioxide is not correctly regulated, which has a detrimental effect on plant growth and survival. Aids to good soil aeration include earthworms, the addition of humus, compost and other organic matter, good drainage, cultivation and mixed cropping.

The Damage Chemicals Do

Chemical fertilizers act as a shot in the arm for plants to start with, but their action, especially when used repeatedly and in large quantities, is responsible for deterioration of soil friability (crumbliness), destruction of beneficial soil life (earthworms, bacteria and so on), alteration of the availability to plants of nutritional elements and thus increased vulnerability to disease and insect attack.

In small amounts the chlorides and sulphates in chemical fertilizers act as plant stimulants, but they are poisonous to the soil organisms and stimulate soil bacteria to such abnormally high reproduction that they use up organic matter faster than it can be returned by chemical agricultural practice, which provides only a small number of the range of nutrients depleted, and also leads to the loss of topsoil, as in the dust bowls in the USA. The high levels of sodium from sodium nitrate fertilizers concentrate in soil water and pull fluid from bacterial and fungal cells causing them to collapse and die, and many artificial fertilizers contain significant quantities of sulphuric and hydrochloric acids from the manufacturing process which increases the acidity of the soil and kills worms. Chemical fertilizers have a negative effect on every natural process which contributes to healthy soil.

Trace minerals are frequently deficient when plants are grown in soil continually treated with artificial fertilizers. This occurs because the colloidal humus particles through which minerals are transferred from the soil to root hairs and into the plant become negatively charged and attract the positive elements such as calcium, potassium, sodium, magnesium, manganese, boron and iron, causing an imbalance. Sodium nitrate added to the soil on a regular basis causes a change in the humus particles since the excessive amount of sodium ions eventually crowds out the other elements making them less available for plant use. The humus becomes coated with sodium and inundates root hairs with the excess. The plants become unable to pick up the minerals they really need. As a result, plants grown with artificial fertilizers frequently have a lower nutrient value than their organically grown counterparts. Experiments have revealed that, for instance, supplying citrus fruit trees with quantities of highly soluble nitrogen lowers the vitamin C content of oranges. It also lowers the capacity of hybrid corn to produce seeds with a high protein content.

How to Rebuild Healthy Soil

It is important to begin by finding out what kind of soil you have to work with. Any garden centre will have home soil-test kits which allow you to find out the pH of the soil and the nitrogen, phosphorus and potassium levels. The pH level of the soil represents its acidity or alkalinity and may range from a pH factor of approximately 4.5 to 8 depending upon your location. On the pH scale of 1 to 14, 1 to 6 are acidic and sour, 7 is neutral, and 8 to 14 are alkaline and sweet. The horticultural neutral is pH 6.5; most plants prefer a slightly acid to neutral soil, between about 5.5 and 7.

Some plants, notably azaleas, rhododendrons, heathers, camellias and fuchsias, prefer a more acid soil. Potatoes will grow in very acid soil and turnips in very alkaline, but most vegetables grow best in a slightly alkaline medium; soft fruits, however, prefer a slightly acid soil.

Calcified seaweed makes soil more alkaline, as does the addition of 'lime' or ground limestone. Alkaline soils can be made less alkaline by the addition of manures. Any compost heap left to its own devices will produce an acid humus due to the natural process of decay forming humic acid and the acid nature of most leaves, green stuffs and manure.

Plant disease is linked with soil pH. For instance, scab on potatoes is worse when they are grown in a soil which is too alkaline, and club root is more prevalent when soil is too acid. Pines and other plants or shrubs which grow best in a more acid soil will become unhealthy when planted in a very alkaline environment.

Making Compost

Making your own compost heap is the best way to nourish the soil and it means that you recycle garden and household vegetable wastes while cutting down the burden on our overloaded refuse disposal systems. Composting imitates nature's way of rebuilding soil by encouraging the decomposition of organic substances, but it does it more rapidly because microbes, worms and heat combine to speed up the process.

Any organic gardening book will provide details on building a compost heap using wood slats, breeze blocks or plastic bins with holes punched in the sides. The heap is built in layers and should sit on criss-crossed fibrous material such as twigs or prunings to encourage a good air supply at the bottom of the heap. This is then followed by layers of organic materials including grass clippings, leaves, manure, mouldy hay, wood shavings, washed seaweed, chopped weeds (picked before going to seed), vegetable and fruit scraps, nut and egg shells. Coffee grounds contain nitrogen, phosphorus and potash and insect repelling compounds, and banana skins provide phosphorus and potassium. The heat generated in the centre of the compost heap kills most seeds and weeds.

Avoid using horse manure from sources where worming drugs and chemical feeds are used. Cow manure from an organic farm or from Cowpact Products is a healthier alternative (see p. 255). Sawdust may be added, but check that the wood has not been treated with ammonium sulphate or other chemicals that are fatal to earthworms. Avoid using coal ashes because, although they will lighten heavy soil, there is the danger of contamination with toxic quantities of sulphur and iron.

Composting involves the bacterial and fungal breakdown of waste organic materials. For this to occur efficiently the microorganisms need heat, moisture, nitrogen, air and a proper mixture of materials.

To make your compost heap:

☐ Add earthworms. Just a handful will be sufficient since they breed rapidly.

☐ Mix compost from a well rotted heap into the material.

☐ Add herbs such as yarrow and chamomile, comfrey and nettles. They will help it to rot faster.

☐ Include chopped banana skins. They are rich in bacteria which aids the rapid decomposition of the compost material.

☐ Add a thin layer of topsoil to each layer to hold in the heat.

☐ Chop or cut materials before composting – coarse materials decay slowly and are slow to heat. Microbes that break down the matter go to work faster when the surfaces are broken, and it also makes turning the heap easier.

☐ Mix in seaweed, dried blood, manure and even grass clippings (avoid these if lawn chemicals have been used) so as to increase the nitrogen content of the compost and feed the bacteria which break the material down.

☐ Include fibrous material such as straw to prevent the compost from turning to slime.

When you need to reduce the acidity of the compost, a little lime can be sprinkled into the layers. The heap should be turned once or twice to increase aeration, and when the weather is very dry it should be dampened occasionally, but beware – a waterlogged pile will not heat and will putrefy rather than decay. If the pile is too small, heat does not build up in the centre and decomposition is extremely slow; heat is also important in killing many organisms, weed seeds and viruses. Some gardeners add fish scraps and meat for their nitrogen content, but this is a matter of personal choice.

Your compost heap is ready when:

☐ The material is moderately loose and crumbly and the colour of the compost is black-brown.

☐ The smell is earth-like. Any bad odour is a sign that fermentation has not reached its final goal and that bacterial breakdown processes are still going on. A musty smell indicates the presence of mould or overheating which leads to loss of nitrogen. In this instance, aerate the heap better or start again, adding more fibrous material and keeping it drier.

☐ The pH is neutral or slightly acid – too acid a condition is the result of lack of air and too much moisture. Nitrogen fixing bacteria and earthworms prefer neutral to slightly acid. The pH range of good compost is 6.0–7.4. It is unlikely that a heap will be too alkaline unless too much lime or alkaline material has been added; it naturally decomposes on the acid side.

The compost heap usually becomes 'ripe' in about three to four months.

Humus is organic matter that has reached a more advanced stage of decomposition than compost in the early stages. It acts as a sponge to retain moisture, holds soil particles together as tilth, and darkens the soil which helps it to warm faster in the spring. Add it to the soil to enrich it before planting.

Compost can be spread on top of the soil and hoed in lightly to encourage the surface soil life. Feeder roots from tender plants are able to reach the compost and draw out its nutrients. When applying compost to a vegetable garden it should be dug in during the autumn or buried in furrows when planting and in holes when transplanting. When plants begin to surface, an equal amount of compost mixed with soil can be used as a top dressing or mulch.

Liquid fertilizer can be made from compost, and green leafy matter, particularly stinging nettles, comfrey leaves or washed seaweed etc. Add the organic material to a plastic dustbin three-quarters full of water, preferably rain water. Cover and stir every other day for about two weeks then strain off the soil matter and add it to your compost heap and use the liquid as a feed. When it is made with nettles it can also be used as a spray for aphids.

Garden crops respond well to applications of manure. It can be applied in a quantity of approximately 25 lb of manure fixed with 10 lb of rock phosphate for every 100 sq. ft of garden. If manure is not well rotted it should be applied three or more weeks before planting and incorporated well into the soil, otherwise it can result in leggy or 'burned' plants. Nitrogen is 'fixed' (integrated) during decomposition of manure and the solubility of phosphorus is also made greater.

Natural and organic fertilizers do not overwhelm plants with large amounts of one particular nutrient since they consist of a mix of plant and animal materials converted by bacterial and natural decomposition processes into a medium which is easily taken up by plant roots. If you want to know in more detail what condition your soil is in, Elm Farm Research Centre, Hamstead Marshall, Newbury, Berks (0488 58298) can do a special soil test for deficiency in the main elements for organic gardeners. They also test soil for its lead content – this is extremely important if you live near a large town or close to a road and you want to grow vegetables and fruit on your land.

By noticing the symptoms plants exhibit you can identify and therefore redress an imbalance by adding natural elements. The chart below lists some of the most common problems. For more detailed information consult a good organic gardening book.

Chart 4.4 The main soil nutrients and their sources

Element	Natural Source	Deficiency/Excess
Calcium	Calcified seaweed, ground limestone, dolomite, chalk	*Excess:* soil that is too alkaline.
Magnesium	Dolomite lime	*Excess* (unlikely unless purposely added): soil that is too alkaline.
Nitrogen (N)	Manure, compost, sludge, vegetable meals, dried blood, fish meal, bone meal, seaweed meal, liquid manure made from comfrey leaves	*Deficiency:* yellowing of leaves, stunted growth. *Excess:* delayed flowering, elongation of stems, reduced quality of fruit, renders crops less resistant to disease, aphid attack more likely.
Phosphorus (P)	Rock phosphate, bone meal, dried blood, wood	*Deficiency:* unusually thin or small with

Phosphorus (P) (continued)	ashes, fish	purplish foliage; unhealthy root system, delayed maturity, sterile seed.
Potassium (K Potash)	Green manuring with deep rooted plants like clover or alfalfa (see below); seaweed, kelp, liquid manure made from comfrey leaves	*Deficiency:* slow growth, stunted, browning of leaves, under-sized fruit, poor disease resistance, pale coloured fruit; firing at leaf edges resulting in shrivelled, sterile leaves. Mixed chemical fertilizers tend to increase potassium and decrease magnesium. *Excess:* blocks uptake of other minerals.
Trace elements	Compost, leaf mould, mulch, natural ground rock fertilizers, lime, seaweed, green compost, alfalfa, comfrey leaves, clover (see below), humus	*Deficiency:* plants grown in soil lacking trace elements tend to be weaker and more vulnerable to insect attack.

'Green manuring' involves growing plants such as those listed in the chart under potassium specifically for turning back into the soil. Green manures add organic matter to soils prior to planting and protect the soil from erosion, keep in warmth and moisture and encourage worms. Sow alfalfa April to July, clover April to August, mustard March to September, and winter beans September to November. Dig them in to the soil before maturity.

If you use peat to help retain moisture in the soil and build up its structure, consider using substitutes such as leaf mould, bark, animal manure and compost. Peat bogs are one of Britain's threatened habitats and they are being destroyed rapidly to provide peat for gardening.

PEST CONTROL

Building up soil immunity takes time, but there are plenty of natural defences to draw on rather than resorting to drowning the garden with chemicals and setting it back several years again. It is important to remember that insects are not all pests. They have their place in nature, and whether chemicals are used or not they will always be around, not only as pests, but also as the gardener's ally. One of their more important services is the pollination of plants – although some seed-bearing plants are pollinated by the wind, the majority are fertilized by insects, and this is particularly significant for fruits and vegetables. Another important function of predatory insects is that they kill many of the gardener's enemies by laying their eggs in grubs or caterpillars and destroying them or by stalking and eating them.

It makes no sense at all to attack aphids with powerful insecticides such as dichlorvos, lindane or malathion. Whenever aphids are killed, so are their predators. Organic gardening simply involves establishing a balance. The following chart provides some basic tips which will help you to reduce pests without using toxic products, and without upsetting the natural ecology of the garden.

Chart 4.5 Natural ways to control pests

Pest	Natural Control
Ants	Place bone meal around plants or use cayenne pepper in warm water as a spray. Plant tansy and mint in affected areas and around doorways to discourage ants from entering the house. Ants are associated with aphid infestation as they carry them into plants.
Aphids	Use compost on the soil to produce strong, healthy plants, and grow nasturtiums among the plants. Encourage aphid predators like ladybirds, lacewing flies and hoverflies into the garden (see below) and avoid

using insecticides. Put foil around the bottom of plants or spray with warm soapy* water. Ants carry aphids into plants, so check the ant population in your garden.

*Use soft soap not regular household soap. This is available from HDRA – see p.256.

Cabbage root fly	Place wood ashes around each plant stem to create an alkaline area, and surround the plants with companions including tomatoes, sage, tansy, rosemary, catnip and hyssop. Alternatively, make collars from 5"-high strips of roofing tar paper, place them around young plants, burying them up to 1" in the soil. Secure with a rubber band or string.
Carrot fly	A collar, such as that described under cabbage root fly, will help to keep carrot fly from laying eggs in the soil around plants.
Cutworms	These yellow underwing moth larvae chew plants off at ground level and work at night. Their biggest enemies are toads and bantam hens. Keep down weeds around plants and grasses in which the moth lays its eggs. Interplant with onions and use the collars described under cabbage root fly.
Dogs and cats	Cats and dogs who favour your flowerbed or organic garden as a public convenience are repelled when cayenne pepper is sprinkled liberally in the area. They are also averse to garlic and other strong smelling herbs; these can be interplanted or used as a spray.
Mosquitos	Introducing predators such as toads and frogs can help to reduce mosquitos, as can goldfish ponds as goldfish eat mosquito larvae. Eliminate unwanted buckets or pools of stagnant water.
Parasitic worms	Using compost consistently will help to eliminate nematodes by encouraging the formation of healthy roots and strong plants. Interplant with marigolds.

Rabbits	Rabbits are strictly vegetarian so placing dried blood in borders and around plants will discourage them from eating plants and vegetables. Alternatively, spray the area with a solution of water and dried blood. This will have to be repeated after rain, but three applications should be enough to discourage them.
Red spider mites	Ensure good air circulation around plants and remove any colonies by pressure-spraying with warm water containing onion juice, especially on the underside of the leaves. Ladybirds are red spider mites' adversary. If necessary, pyrethrum dust can be used as a control.
Slugs and snails	Snails and slugs dislike sand, wood ashes, ashes, gravel, lime and other abrasive or corrosive substances. A ring of any of these materials sprinkled around vulnerable plants or scattered in the vegetable garden will help to deter them. Saucers of stale beer (Kaliber works best) sunk into the ground attract slugs and snails in large numbers. Hedgehogs, birds, toads and tortoises eath both these pests. Slugs hide under damp debris and mulches, so cut back trailing leaves etc., and keep the soil bare in spring so they have nowhere to hide while young plants are becoming established.
Woodlice	Eliminate logs, boards and other material that is not needed in the garden. Frogs eat woodlice and they can also be discouraged with a light sprinkling of lime. Although not a serious threat to plants or vegetables, they can reach annoying proportions.
Wireworms	Good drainage is one key to keeping wireworms under control. Enrich soil with compost and earthworms to improve aeration. Radishes and turnips can be planted as a decoy, or trap crop. Alfalfa planted repeatedly as green manure will gradually reduce wireworms.

Encouraging Natural Predators

> If using biological controls it is necessary to tolerate a few pests as food for the predators.

☐ **Ladybirds** are predatory insects and both the larvae (which resemble tiny alligators) and the adults feed heavily on aphids, scale insects, red spider mites and the eggs and larvae of small pests. If the garden is sprayed with chemical insecticides ladybirds are killed.

☐ **Lacewing flies** are important allies in the garden as both adults and larvae eat small insects, mites and larvae. They can also live on certain high-protein foods such as pollen and nectar. Any cover crop that supplies these will encourage lacewings into the garden.

☐ **Hoverflies** can be encouraged into the garden by avoiding chemical sprays and planting flowers such as marigolds, asters and cornflowers. Hoverflies eat numerous insects including aphids (blackfly and greenfly).

☐ **Wasps** are garden predators. Many a stung picnicker has probably questioned their worth, but they are helpful to the organic gardener. Some species lay their eggs in other insect eggs; the hatched parasite then causes the destruction of the host by eating it.

☐ Mature **frogs** feed on numerous insects and woodlice. They can be raised from tadpoles in a garden pond or turned loose in a moist spot in the garden if already mature.

☐ **Toads** are voracious garden predators. They are nocturnal feeders and are especially fond of small slugs, although they will eat almost any pest which ventures out during night hours. They do eat earthworms, but if the soil is healthy and well populated with worms the toads will more than earn their keep. Collect tadpoles when nearly mature and put them in a shallow container of water in the garden under a shrub or bush. The clay dishes from plant pots are ideal. Toads can live up to 10 years, and many will survive and stay in the garden if there is plenty of moisture.

☐ Encouraging **birds**, **bees** and **hoverflies** into the garden helps to keep down the pest population. Birds consume a huge number of insects as part of their diet, including those on the underside of leaves. Swallows, for example, sweep the sky for nocturnal insects, wrens eat tiny insect eggs and aphids, thrushes eat snails, and robins hunt soil pests. It is true that they also devour your seedlings and fruit, but this can be offset by protecting small plants with netting and growing ornamental berries which birds favour over cultivated varieties. Consider growing elder, cotoneaster, rowan and other ornamental berry-bearing trees and shrubs. Using slug pellets like metaldehyde can kill birds by secondary poisoning when they eat snails and slugs poisoned by these chemicals.

Learn how to encourage a variety of birds into the garden by contacting the Royal Society for the Protection of Birds (RSPB – listed on p.000) and asking for their booklets *Feeding Garden Birds* and *Gardening for Birds* and their information sheets on shrubs, trees and birds. Put feeders out all year, make nesting material available and provide plenty of water for bathing and drinking. Specific food items will encourage particular birds; for instance, all varieties of tit – very fond of pests like aphids – will feed happily on half a coconut suspended from a tree.

Many butterflies are losing their natural woodland habitats and consequently their populations are decreasing. They are attracted by numerous flowers, especially wild varieties, but some of them, the cabbage white for example, are unfortunately serious pests as the caterpillars feed on vegetables. Other caterpillars have a secretion that is 'milked' by ants, which in turn carry them into plants. Moths can also be a problem to gardeners, with some species' caterpillars feeding on plants including turnips and potatoes, and others attacking fruit trees and bushes. The magpie moth, nicknamed the currant moth, is a serious pest of currant bushes and apricot trees, and the codling moth's caterpillar burrows into apples. If birds populate your garden, the caterpillars will become their food and will only be a minor problem, in which case you can grow a patch of nettles and wildflowers in a corner of the garden to encourage butterflies.

The following charts overleaf list some of the plants and herbs which specifically attract natural predators into your garden.

Using Plants as Pest Deterrents

Plants get by better with a little help from their friends. Companion planting discourages pests and encourages healthier plants. Insects can be either repelled or attracted by colours, sounds and smells; successful gardening involves mixing plants so as to make use of these effects. Spreading herbs among the vegetables, or garlic among flowerbeds will, at the very least, break up their appeal to pests.

> A garden or area for growing one kind of plant is a sitting target for particular pests. In mixed plantings the pests are less likely to reach epidemic proportions.

Some herbs effectively fend off insect attacks and many are immune to attack themselves. Some will discourage insects over a wide area if interplanted; depending on the size and type of plant, the protective range can vary from one to three feet. For instance, tansy, a strong insect repellant, can be grown in perennial borders and backgrounds. In medieval times it was scattered in straw floor coverings to repel troublesome insects and mites.

Most insect-repelling plants not only deter pests, but also have practical home uses. Feverfew from the chrysanthemum/ pyrethrum family can be picked and added to sandwiches if you suffer from headaches and migraines; mature lavender can be used to make moth-repelling sachets for clothing, and pyrethrum daisy is widely cultivated as a source of insecticide. Chamomile flowers can be dried and used as a calming and relaxing tea or as a skin tonic and soother, and pennyroyal extracts repel fleas and can be used safely on pets and their bedding.

Onions and garlic interplant successfully. Onions are attacked when planted in regimental rows so it is best to mix them with flowers and other vegetables to prevent the build-up of

Chart 4.6 What to plant to encourage natural predators

Herb/Flower/Wildflower	Bees	Birds	Butterflies	Hoverflies
Alyssum	✓			
Anchusa	✓			
Anise hyssop	✓			
Borage	✓			
Buddleia			✓	
Buttercup	✓		✓	
Candytuft			✓	
Canterbury bells	✓			
Catnip	✓			
Chives	✓			
Clary sage	✓			
Clover	✓		✓	
Convolvulus	✓		✓	✓
Dahlia	✓			✓
Dill				✓
Eschscholzia				✓
Fennel				
Field scabious	✓	✓	✓	
Forget-me-not	✓			
Gentian	✓		✓	
Heliotrope	✓		✓	
Honesty	✓	✓	✓	
Hyssop	✓		✓	
Knapweed	✓	✓	✓	
Lady's-smock	✓		✓	
Lavender	✓			
Mallow	✓		✓	
Marigold (calendula)				✓
Marjoram	✓			
Mesembryanthemum	✓			
Mint	✓			
Pennyroyal	✓			
Poached egg plant	✓			✓
Ragged robin			✓	
Rosemary	✓			
Sage	✓			
Savory	✓			
Sunflower	✓	✓		
Sweet rocket	✓	✓		
Sweet scabious			✓	
Thyme	✓			
Trefoil	✓			
Vetch	✓		✓	
Wallflowers	✓			

Chart 4.7 Plants which deter insects

Herb/Plant	Insect Deterred
Asters	Most insects
Basil	Flies and mosquitos
Borage	Tomato worm (also improves tomato growth and flavour)
Calendula	Most insects
Catnip	Cabbage whites
Celery	Cabbage whites
Chrysanthemum	Most insects
Garlic	Most insects, blight
Geranium	Most insects
Marigolds*	Most insects
Marjoram	Numerous pests
Mint	Ants
Nasturtium	Aphids, cabbage whites
Onion family	Most insects
Petunia	Protects beans
Peppermint	Cabbage white
Rosemary	Carrot fly, cabbage whites
Rue	Numerous pests, including cabbage whites
Sage	Carrot fly, cabbage whites
Salsify	Carrot fly
Savory	Numerous pests
Tansy	Ants, flying insects
Thyme	Numerous pests

*Dwarf marigolds are just as effective as the larger varieties and do not take up much space or shade smaller plants. Because their insect-repelling qualities need to build up, they may not be very effective in the first year.

Chart 4.8 Good plant companions

Vegetable/Herb	Companion and Insect Controlling Plants
Asparagus	Basil, parsley, tomatoes
Beans	Carrots, celery, cucumber, cauliflower, potatoes, corn, strawberries, most herbs
Beetroot	Garlic, onions, cabbage family
Cabbage family	Celery, dill, chamomile, sage, peppermint, rosemary, beetroot, onions. Cabbage whites are repelled by nasturtiums, tomatoes, catnip, rosemary and sage planted amongst the cabbages
Carrots	Chives, lettuce, onions, peas, rosemary, leeks, tomatoes
Celery	Beans, cauliflower, cabbage, leeks, tomatoes
Cucumbers	Beans, peas, radishes, sunflowers
Lettuce	Carrots, radishes, strawberries, onions
Onions	Beetroot, chamomile, lettuce, strawberries, tomatoes
Parsley	Asparagus, tomatoes
Peas	Carrots, beans, cucumbers, turnips, radishes, most herbs or vegetables
Potatoes	Beans, cabbage, corn, horseradish (at corners), marigolds
Radish	Cucumbers, lettuce, nasturtiums, peas
Spinach	Strawberries
Strawberries	Beans, borage, lettuce, spinach, thyme
Tomatoes	Asparagus, carrots, chives, marigolds, parsley, nasturtiums, basil
Turnip	Peas

harmful onion fungi, but garlic is almost pest-proof. It is said that planting a ring of garlic around fruit trees may save them from boring insects and it can be rewarding to plant it among flowers and vegetables. Initially garlic is relatively expensive, but one clove becomes a bulb of garlic which can then be picked and stored for use all through the winter to ward off colds and infections.

Plants can also be used as traps or decoys with the basic aim being to attract rather than repel insects. Trap plants act as hosts to pests and draw them away from the plants you want left alone. Clover and alfalfa are both attractive to aphids and a patch of either planted near vulnerable plants will lure pests away. These also add nitrogen to the soil and make potent compost when dug in at the end of the season.

The chart opposite outlines some plant companions which benefit each other. It will help further to study the plants you are growing in order to become acquainted with their root systems. Growing together plants which both have spreading, shallow roots will cause them to compete and produce weak plants that insects attack. Some plants are definitely not compatible: fennel should not be planted near tomatoes or bush beans, and kohlrabi and tomatoes are best kept apart too.

Monoculture is an open invitation to insect pests, virus diseases and fungus. Keep plants with similar root structures away from each other, and move annual plantings from place to place. Diversification brings about balance in insect populations and prevents depletion in the soil of any one particular nutrient.

Crop rotation is a vital part of organic gardening and simply involves moving crops to different areas of the garden each year. This helps with the soil's nutrient content and prevents specific insects and plant diseases from becoming well established. Different plants require varying quantities of nutrients and those which send down deep roots help by bringing up minerals normally unavailable to shallow rooted varieties. Squash requires a great deal of nitrogen, while peas manufacture most of their own — facts like these can be taken into consideration when deciding

where and what to relocate. A general principle is to plant heavy
feeders first. Leafy vegetables such as lettuce, cabbage, tomatoes,
cauliflower and broccoli are heavy feeders and should be planted
in a well fertilized soil. These can be followed by root crops such
as carrots, beets and turnips which are light feeders.

Reducing the numbers of particular pests using parasites,
predators and species-specific diseases is known as biological
control. It can be a very effective and safe way to remove pests
without resorting to chemicals. For more details, and to purchase
species-specific diseases, see the Henry Doubleday Research Association catalogue (p.256).

Natural Pest-repelling Sprays

Sprays are not exclusively the domain of the chemical gardener;
the organic gardener, too, can concoct some potent insecticides –
but from harmless ingredients. One of the most effective ways to
remove aphids like black or greenfly is to spray them with warm
soapy water from a hand pressure spray. This also works for house
plants and will not contaminate edible crops. Ensure that the
underside of leaves are sprayed. It may take up to three separate
applications over several days to combat the little horrors, but it
works. Use soft soap which is available from HDRA (listed on
p.256), not detergents or regular household soap. Ecover washing-
up liquid (see Chapter 8) also works well. Use approximately one
bar of soft soap dissolved in a pint of boiling water, then add to
five gallons of cold water.

Other home-made sprays can be produced from garden plants
and kitchen items. To remove aphids from roses you can make a
spray from feverfew and chopped onions with soft soap; chewing
insects are repelled by a spray made from Ecover washing-up liquid
and hot peppers; and an all-purpose spray can be made with garlic,
ground onions, tansy, pyrethrum, cayenne pepper, and soft soap.
There is great scope for experimentation.

To make a spray, cover the mashed materials with water and
leave for twelve hours. Strain and add enough water to make up
a gallon. Dissolve 1 oz of soft soap in the liquid. The mash that
you strain off can be added to the compost heap or buried around
affected plants. The sprays should be used several times a day for

about three days. Caffeinated filter coffee has a pesticidal effect
and can be made into a spray, or the grounds can be mixed with
the soil in your house plants to repel creepy crawlies. They also
supply nitrogen.

The Last Resort

There are now products being marketed that are less destructive to predators (ladybirds, lacewings, hoverflies etc.) – their
persistence and potency tends to be less than that of synthetic chemical products. You can also buy safer botanical sprays
derived from plant substances. They are recommended by the
Soil Association as a last resort because they are not completely
without problems: some do kill bees and other wildlife; but they
are relatively safe for adults, children and animals and some may
be used in roof spaces since they do not kill bats.

Pyrethrum and Rotenone are two plant-derived substances
recommended by the Soil Association if you *have* to spray.
Read the label when you buy these because a boost chemical,
usually methoxychlor, is often added to give more lasting effects.
The Henry Doubleday Research Association (HDRA – see p.256)
sells pure versions of these sprays.

Both pyrethrum and rotenone are toxic to certain insects
(including ladybirds) but less dangerous to animals, pets, birds
or humans. Pyrethrin is found mainly in the developing seeds of
pyrethrum, which resembles a daisy. It is also effective against
flies, and in the home it discourages cockroaches. It can be
grown easily in the garden; its Latin name is *Chrysanthemum
cinerariaefolium*.

Rotenone is often combined with pyrethrum and is effective
against caterpillars, keeping them off plants but not killing them
– it lasts for about three days. It comes from the roots of a number
of tropical trees and climbing plants which produce it for their own
protection against insects.

Derris powder comes from a root in the East Indies and
also contains rotenone. It acts on contact and as a stomach
poison and may be used against aphids, thrips, red spider mites,

caterpillars, certain larvae and destructive beetles. It is harmful to wildlife but has a very short persistence. Since it is poisonous to fish, it should be used with great care near ponds and streams. It is relatively non-toxic to bees but spraying should be avoided when plants are in flower and bees are working.

Quassia is an alkaloid of great bitterness derived from a Jamaican tree, *Picrasma quassioides*. It can be obtained from the Henry Doubleday Research Association in the form of wood chips which are boiled with water to produce a spray. It is a mild product that acts mainly as an antifeedant on small caterpillars by making the plant taste extremely unattractive to them. Mixed with soft soap it can be used against aphids.

Sulphur is an excellent fungicide and can be used to control mildew and deter mites, worms and aphids, allowing young plants to get ahead. Use only the simplest sulphur and a little lime to dust young cabbages and broccoli.

WEEDS

Weeds are the scourge of organic gardening. Resorting to the use of chemical weedkillers certainly gets rid of weeds, but the chemicals systematically murder soil bacteria and kill flowers, shrubs and other plants. Weeds have to be pulled out or dug up once they become established, so prevention is always better than cure.

Mulches are frequently used to prevent weeds from growing. This involves covering soil with manure, straw, grass clippings, shredded or whole leaves, hay, wood chips, or even old carpet, which can be used upside down on the soil from March onwards. Some gardeners find that aluminium foil makes a superb mulch which also encourages plant growth and discourages aphids. Photodegradable plastic bags can be used as mulch and *will* biodegrade in your garden; as they do not decompose in landfill sites, this is a good opportunity to recycle them.

Mulches of all kinds keep weeds down, soil loose, prevent rain erosion and stop rapid moisture loss in hot weather. Lay the material on the ground, make holes and plant seedlings through it with a handful of compost. Organic mulches gradually break down feeding nutrients into the soil as an added benefit. A one-inch layer of sawdust can be laid down when vegetable plants are three to four inches tall, but nitrogen-rich materials should be used at the same time in the soil because sawdust decomposition tends to produce a temporary nitrogen shortage. Tomato plants do particularly well with this mulch.

Once an organic garden has been established, the rewards and satisfaction are worth all the toil and disappointments in the first few years. The garden will still contain insect pests but the predators will keep them at reasonable levels, and healthy soil will produce plants that are far less attractive to most pests. Learn to encourage wildlife into the garden, not only for the removal of pests, but also for the pleasure of watching birds and butterflies.

No matter how small your garden you can still grow healthy organic vegetables and plants – see *The Quantum Carrot* – and even window boxes and grow-bags give you scope to create a micro organic garden.

For a list of useful addresses and suppliers of green gardening products, see under 'Gardening Products' (p.255) in Chapter 8.

Further Reading

Gardening Without Chemicals, Jack Temple (Thorsons, 1986).

Grow More Vegetables, John Jeavons (Berkeley Ten Speed Press, 1982). Obtainable from the Soil Association.

Natural Pest and Disease Control, Jim Hay (Century, 1987).

Organic Gardening Magazine, available from PO Box 4, Wiveliscombe, Taunton, Somerset, TA4 2QY. Telephone (0984) 23998.

Successful Organic Pest Control, Trevor G. Forsythe (Thorsons, 1990).

The Quantum Carrot, Branton Kenton (Ebury, 1987).

Vegetables Naturally, Jim Hay (Century, 1985).

Tracking Down Other Hazards

Multiple or high level exposure to chemicals such as pesticides
or herbicides or excessive exposure to an individual substance
may predispose some people to chemical allergies.

Symptoms related to chemical sensitivity are usually obscure and
sometimes debilitating. Until quite recently chemically induced
illness was rarely diagnosed or identified as such, and some sufferers have run the gamut from suspecting food allergies, taking
tranquillizers or shovelling down handfuls of randomly chosen
vitamin pills to undergoing years of psychoanalysis in an attempt
to feel better.

Karen's case history is typical of unsuspected chemical sensitivity. She noticed the development of a severe headache and
depression whenever she visited a particular relative and at first
she attributed it to not enjoying the visits. Friends agreed that it
seemed a logical explanation and she dismissed the headache as
a psychological reaction. As time passed she noticed a similar
headache and depression whenever she spent the afternoon with
a friend who insisted on cooking the family's dinner while they
talked, and the same symptoms developed at work towards the
end of the day. As the winter progressed she started to notice
them in her own home, especially at night. The headache steadily
became worse, and began to be accompanied by irritability and
occasional bouts of panic, which prompted her to seek medical
help. She emerged labelled as 'stressed' and with a prescription
for a tranquillizer. It didn't help. She found it difficult to understand why the headaches became more severe during the winter
and gradually eased as the summer arrived, and was particularly
puzzled that they did not occur at all when visiting the relative
in the summer.

Her battery of medicines expanded by the month until she was
taking four separate prescriptions, but the headache and depres-

sion, together with the side effects, began to make it difficult for her to function. Her last resort was to visit a natural practitioner who suggested that environmental factors might be causing the problem. This sparked her to investigate the areas where she was aware of the headaches developing, and she discovered to her surprise that gas featured in every situation. The relative used a gas space heater in the living room all through the winter, her friend cooked with gas, the kitchen at work had gas rings with a pilot light and in her own home a gas waterheater was situated on the landing opposite her bedroom.

To test her theory she spent a week with her brother because the house had no gas appliances, and for the first time in two years the headache and depression gradually disappeared. She now visits her friend when she is not cooking, shuts the door to the kitchen at the office and has moved her desk next to a window which she keeps open. In the winter she spends time with the relative during the morning when the sun warms the room and the heater is off, and she has replaced the gas waterheating system in her home with an electric immersion heater. Further investigation into her case history led to the discovery that the sensitivity to gas (or its combustion chemicals) coincided with the development of a chronic candida yeast infection.

> Depression has been specifically linked to exposure to gas and the combustion products of gas, oil and coal in the home.
>
> *Journal of Laboratory and Clinical Medicine*

Multiple or high-level exposure to toxic chemicals such as herbicides and pesticides or excessive exposure to an everyday substance may predispose some people to chemical allergies. Even chemical cleaning products kept under the sink can release enough chemicals into the air to affect an extra chemically sensitive person if ventilation is poor. Most people don't suspect that leakage can occur from bottles and cans. Allergies may also develop after a severe bout of flu or as a result of a yeast infection such as candida. All these factors cause weakening of the immune system, which is explained in more detail in Chapter 7.

Chemical sensitivities can range from a sniffle or constant

nasal drip (as can classical allergies) to severe symptoms like blackouts. Chronic chemical exposure does not automatically result in the manifestation of chemical sensitivity, but researchers are beginning to suspect that, regardless of whether a person develops physical symptoms or not, constant exposure to particular chemicals, especially in industrial situations, may still harm the body. Their advice is to limit chemical exposure whenever possible, even if exposure does not result in the development of physical symptoms.

Reactions to chemicals in buildings are likely to be worse in the winter when, as well as ventilation being decreased, heating encourages the release of chemicals. A shopping trip can expose the body to high levels of potential pollutants. This may be one reason why people who feel fine at home suffer from irritability and headaches when they visit an enclosed shopping centre or particular areas within department stores. The Christmas rush may not be the only reason for people's increased irritability at this time.

> 'It has been noted that in many instances food and chemicals sensitivities seem to elicit the same list of behaviours and physical symptoms as have been considered characteristic of the neuroses.'
>
> *Clinical Ecology Vol. III No. 2*

Despite the number of chemicals we are faced with, we are still generally healthier than our ancestors; all the same, chemical toxicants are beginning to establish themselves as a very real threat to overall health.

TROUBLE SPOTS

If you are aware of chemical sensitivities but have been unable to track them down, the information which follows may provide clues to help solve the problem. (You can refer back to the Data Sheets in Chapter 2 – pp. 24 ff – for detailed information about the chemicals printed in **bold**.) If any of the symptoms linked with

situations in the chart apply to you, check the key which follows
to find out what might be causing them and to learn how to cut
down the risks of adverse reactions.

**Chart 5.1 Common trouble spots for people with chemical
sensitivity**

Environment	Some Common Symptoms
Bathroom	Headache, lethargy, depression
Bedroom	Eye, nose and throat irritation, lethargy, heart palpitations, headache, irritability, depression
Clothes shops, furniture stores, enclosed shopping centres, carpet departments or carpet warehouses	Headache, depression, burning eyes, tightness in the chest or difficulty breathing, palpitations, dry or sore throat, irritability, nasal congestion
Dry-cleaners	Headache, mental confusion, depression, fatigue
Hairdressing salons	Irritability, headache, depression, fatigue, confusion, intoxicated sensation, extreme tiredness, floating sensation, inability to concentrate
Kitchen	Headache, depression, nausea, decreased coordination, dizziness, nose and throat irritation, heart palpitations, weakness, fatigue, decreased sense of smell
Living room	Fatigue, tiredness, headache, depression, irritability, dizziness, drowsiness, heart palpitations, nasal congestion, burning eyes, irritation of eyes, nose and throat
Offices	Lethargy, tension headaches, depression, irritability, mental and

Offices (continued)	physical fatigue, dizziness, irritation of nose, throat, and eyes, conditions similar to hay fever, worsening of asthma and other respiratory problems
Perfume departments	Nausea, blocked or streaming nose, headache, depression, anxiety, joint pains
Petrol stations and exhaust fumes	Headache, depression, nausea, dizziness, heart palpitations, fatigue, weakness
Print and copy shops	Nausea, headache, depression, giddiness, irritability, tightness of chest, irritation of eyes, nose and throat, disorientation, tiredness
TV and electrical appliance showrooms	Tiredness, dizziness, irritability, headache, depression, disorientation, dry throat or eyes

Key

☒ Bathroom

The bathroom harbours numerous potential allergens and chemicals. **Mould** may grow in corners and ceilings, and cleaning chemicals and aerosols are frequently stored under the sink – some of which may vaporize into the air in tiny amounts if the temperature is warm enough. Hot water forced through a shower head releases vaporized **chloroform** and **trichloroethylene**, and regularly inhaling clouds of **talcum** powder has been associated with lung disease.

Cut the risks
Showers are best taken with the window open or an extractor fan running, and the bathroom door should be closed to

prevent chemically contaminated steam from entering the air in the rest of the house. The smell of chlorine is often evident when a bath is run, but the release of chloroform and trichloroethylene is undetectable. Gradually phase out aerosols and commercial cleaning products and replace them with the Ecover range (see Chapter 8). Limescale can be tackled with OZ, a safe non-chemical product, and a firm nylon brush with hot water and borax will remove mould. Shower heads, drainpipes and washbasin or bath overflows provide bacteria and mould with an ideal breeding ground due to the warm, damp, dark conditions. Clean these areas regularly with a solution of hot water and borax and rinse them well. Good ventilation and bright light will help to reduce mould and bacterial growth (see also Chapter 2).

⊠ Bedroom

It is common for people to wake up feeling tired and lethargic even after sleeping for eight hours. How many suspect that what they are sleeping with (not counting the partner) could be making them feel like this? Ambient chemicals, mainly **formaldehyde**, released from chipboard and veneered furniture, fitted wardrobes, carpets, fabric dressings and treatments, mingling with dry-cleaning chemicals from newly cleaned clothes in the wardrobe, chemical treatments on leather shoes, perfumes and aerosol products and outgassing from plastics can make the air in a bedroom a veritable chemical soup. At night the body takes the opportunity to throw off or neutralize pollutants and metabolic wastes that have accumulated during the day, but this process is hindered by the chemicals in the air it is also forced to detoxify. The problem is intensified by heating, which dries the air and encourages numerous chemicals to vaporize. If windows are kept closed, chemical vapours may build up to the point where particularly sensitive people wake up feeling unwell, and in others it can contribute to morning grogginess, fatigue and the longing to hibernate.

Cut the risks
If you have recently installed fitted wardrobes or furniture made from veneered chipboard it is possible to cut down the release of

formaldehyde from them by painting any exposed surfaces with a natural plant-based varnish (see Chapter 8). Also review the ventilation in the room, especially during the winter. If you store spray deodorants, hair sprays or perfumes in the bedroom, consider keeping them in a spare bedroom or in the bathroom (if it is well ventilated) as this will decrease chronic exposure to potential allergens. (See the entry on perfume departments below.) Any dry-cleaned items, especially continental quilts, which can hold the powerful solvent vapours in the filling, should be aired outside for at least 24 hours before being brought into a bedroom.

If you buy new clothes, wash them several times before hanging them in a bedroom where you sleep. Wash new sheets and bedding 6 to 7 times using a mixture of biodegradable washing powder and bicarbonate of soda to remove some of the chemicals. Non-iron or easy-care cotton clothing or bedding is treated with a permanent formaldehyde dressing, so if you are attempting to decrease the level of formaldehyde in the home, avoid it by choosing brushed or ironable cotton and use fitted bottom sheets since they stretch and eliminate the need for ironing.

> 'Catatonic states, depression, fatigue and emotional disruption have been demonstrated to occur following exposures to fungus and mould substances.'
>
> *Clinical Ecology, 1976*

Storing books in the bedroom may precipitate allergic reactions since old books can harbour mould, fungus and unseen micro organisms. Using an ionizer (see Chapter 8) in the room will help to alleviate the problem since negative ions generated by the unit clean the air by precipitating airborne dust towards the floor and limiting the growth of mould and fungus.

If a bathroom is attached to the bedroom, it becomes even more important to use only natural and biodegradable cleaning products, since vapours from commercial products will leach into the air in the bedroom, and **chloroform** and **trichloroethylene** released from water during a shower will also find their way into the sleeping area. For more information see the bathroom entry.

A large spider plant will help to reduce levels of formaldehyde in the bedroom (see Chapter 3 for more details).

✖ Clothes shops, furniture stores, enclosed shopping centres, carpet departments or warehouses

The risk in these places is mainly **formaldehyde** exposure from fabric treatments on clothing and furniture and other fabric items, carpets and underlay on shop floors or in displays in carpet shops, chipboard pressed woods and veneers, adhesives, dyes, plastics and plastic-based fabrics like polyester, cleaning chemicals, low levels of negative ions and poor lighting.

Cut the risks
Literally thousands of chemicals may be competing for air space in an enclosed shopping centre or department store and the potential reaction to them is far greater than at home. Larger shopping centres often have a fountain in one area – this is not purely aesthetic. Running water and the breaking of water droplets creates negative ions which purify and refresh the air. If you do suffer from chemical sensitivity and notice yourself becoming bad-tempered, fatigued or developing a headache in a shopping centre, head for the fountain. If the problem is very severe, consider mail-order shopping as an alternative.

✖ Dry-cleaners

Numerous solvents and volatile chemicals are used to remove stains from clothing and dissolve grease. These include **ammonia, benzene, formaldehyde, perchlorethylene, toluene, trichloroethylene, xylene, carbon tetrachloride**.

Cut the risks
The inhalation of some dry-cleaning chemicals sends them straight into the bloodstream, and they may occur in breast milk. If you are feeding a baby or if you react to solvents, limit your exposure to dry-cleaning chemicals, and if you do have items dry-cleaned ventilate the car well when transporting them home. Avoid storing dry-cleaned clothing in your or

a child's bedroom until it has aired for at least 24 hours. If you work in a dry-cleaners, limit your exposure to chemicals as much as possible and insist on good ventilation. Ensure that your diet contains plenty of fresh fruit and vegetables and if possible take up to 250 mg of vitamin C 2 to 3 times a day. Exercise in the fresh air as much as possible to assist the efficiency of the lungs and to oxygenate the blood.

✖ Hairdressing salons

The air in a hairdressing salon can become heavy with perm chemicals which include **ammonia**, hair sprays which are a potent concoction of **plastics (PVP)**, aerosol propellants, **formaldehyde**, chemical fragrance, **talcum** dust and numerous other chemicals. This is compounded by heat from hair dryers which reduces levels of positive ions in the air (see Chapter 3) and reduces humidity. Ventilation in salons is rarely good.

Cut the risks
People who are sensitive to chemicals at the hairdressing salon find that booking the first morning appointment on a Monday enables them to live through an otherwise unpleasant experience. Apart from Wella's 'Novena', herbal perms use the same appalling chemicals as a regular perm – with a smattering of herbal extracts. They are likely to be just as intolerable if you are sensitive to perming chemicals. Decline hair spray and the use of talc on a brush to remove hairs and go out for a walk in the fresh air as soon as the appointment is over. When you arrive home or at the office, open windows and have a cup of hot water and lemon to help your liver detoxify some of the chemicals you have inhaled. Whether you are suffering from symptoms or not, take 500 mg of vitamin C with bioflavinoids, two chlorella tablets and 500 mg of calcium and magnesium – magnesium specifically helps the body to detoxify ammonia, which occurs in perming solutions.

✖ Kitchen

Gas ovens and hotplates represent the main source of pollution in a kitchen due to the release of **carbon monoxide** and **nitro-**

gen dioxide, sulphur dioxide and formaldehyde. Other sources include chipboard and veneered cabinets – which also release formaldehyde – solvents, ammonia and bleach, cleaning products, aerosols, oven cleaners, metal polishes, pesticides and so on stored under the sink, and numerous plastic items, especially PVC tiles and floor coverings. Wall coverings may contain pesticides and mould inhibitors, and a microwave oven with a badly sealed door can leak electromagnetic radiation.

Cut the risks

If you do use a gas oven or gas rings for cooking, it is important to ventilate the kitchen well to prevent gas combustion products from building up in the air. Babies, young children and the elderly are particularly vulnerable to toxic emissions from gas appliances. If you can, fit an externally vented extractor fan and cooker hood over the oven and gas rings. Ensure that all gas appliances are regularly maintained, and if your gas flame burns red/orange rather than blue have the gas board adjust it for you.

Phase out chemical cleaning products and household fluids and gradually replace them with products from the Clearspring (see under Faith Products) and Ecover lines (see Chapter 8, pp.252-3); also see the end of Chapter 2 for home-made cleaning products). Exposed chipboard in cabinets can be painted with a natural varnish (see LIVOS and AURO in Chapter 8) to prevent formaldehyde from vaporizing into the air. As plastic items wear out replace them with stainless steel, ceramic or wood wherever possible and buy plasticizer-free clingfilm. Preferred floor coverings include wood, clay quarry tiles, naturally sealed cork or linoleum. LIVOS (see Chapter 8) carry a non-toxic adhesive.

Have all gas appliances and the microwave oven checked and serviced regularly and consider using a stainless steel pressure cooker as an alternative quick-cooking method to using a microwave. If you can, locate washing machine, dryer and dishwasher in an area separate from the kitchen to reduce the build-up of chlorine and trichloroethylene from hot water. Dryers should always be vented outside and therefore located on an exterior wall.

✖ Living room

Approximately 90 percent of home soft furnishings are filled with
plastic polyurethane foams which are a serious fire hazard and
can release petrochemical vapours into a warm room, especially
when new. Wall-to-wall synthetic carpet and the underlay are a
significant source of **formaldehyde**, and **plastic** items may also
release vapours. TVs, stereo equipment and videos are a source of
low-level radiation and electromagnetic radiation and contribute
to 'stale' air by releasing high levels of positive ions (see Chapter
6); they also dry the air. When warm, the inner components
of electrical items, including the plastic wire casings, release
chemicals.

Polishes and stain-removing fluids used on carpets or furniture
and aerosol air fresheners also contribute to the level of chemicals
in the environment. Coal or wood fireplaces release **benzopyrenes**
and **carbon monoxide** into indoor air, and the 'greenhouse gas'
carbon dioxide outside. Indoor air pollution from fireplaces is
increased by double glazing and draught proofing. A burning fire
causes air to be drawn from around windows and up the chimney
which creates a natural air flow. Double glazing prevents this and
increases the chance of gases backing up into the room.

Cut the risks

Apart from their potential to pollute indoor air, coal or log
fires lose most of the heat up the chimney. A fireplace is more
efficient when an underfloor duct supplies external air and the
smoke is released through a flue with an air damper and smoke
shelf, and pollution can be reduced by using clean-burn solid fuel
rather than wood or regular coal. Keep chimneys swept and clear
of debris, since blockages result in smoke and gases entering the
room. An airtight high-performance stove which runs on coal, oil
or wood is an efficient, low-pollution alternative to the standard
fireplace.

Always ventilate a room when using electrical equipment,
and sit at least 8 to 10 feet away from the TV as radiation
diminishes with distance. (You can measure this with an AM
radio – see p.180). Install an ionizer (see Chapter 8) to counteract

the production of positive ions, freshen the air and reduce static caused by appliances and synthetic carpets.

Foam-padded furniture became popular in the 1960s owing to its relative cheapness, but since then fire fatalities have increased (see Chapter 3 for more information). The home is full of flammable materials. Although cotton also burns, the smoke is less dangerous and it does not release irritating vapours under normal usage. Consider including cotton-filled futons which convert to sofas, and natural fibre fillings in conventional furniture. Manufacturers are now required to use combustion-modified highly resilient foam (CMHR) which burns more slowly than traditional polyurethane foam and gives off fewer fumes.

Commercial polishes and stain removers release solvents and other chemicals into the air, all of which can be irritating and unhealthy if the room is not well ventilated. Efficient alternatives include natural beeswax polishes and other non-chemical cleaning items which do not release chemical vapours and naturally add a pleasant scent to the room. (See LIVOS and Goldreif in Chapter 8, and the end of Chapter 2 for home-made cleaners and polishes.)

Furnishings, fabrics, carpets and underlays are sources of **formaldehyde**. When these items wear, consider replacing them with natural alternatives (see Chapter 8 for inspiration).

✖ Offices

Pollutant chemicals vaporize from furniture, carpets, wall panelling and stationery items; electrostatic charges originate from electrical equipment. High levels of carbon dioxide, ambient chemicals and bad lighting form the basis for sick building syndrome.

Cut the risks

The US National Institute of Safety and Health (NIOSH) have tested photocopiers and found that they emit low levels of **ozone**, **carbon monoxide**, **ammonia**, nitrogen oxides including **nitrogen dioxide** and **selenium oxide**. Keep photocopiers and laser printers in a well ventilated area, preferably in a separate room. If you work close to a photocopier – move, or open windows where possible.

Smoking produces numerous irritants and carcinogens and non-smokers are subjected to unavoidable side-stream smoke which is carcinogenic and an irritant. For information on stopping smoking and your rights as an employee to work in a smoke-free area, contact: Action on Smoking and Health (ASH), 5–11 Mortimer Street, London. Enclose a large SAE with your enquiry. (Also see Integration, listed under Health Groups in Chapter 8.)

Drop some hints to the person in charge of ordering the stationery about finding non-toxic felt pens and glues. Replace correcting fluids containing **1.1.1-trichloroethane** with a safer brand like Opti. Spray mounts and other aerosols propel tiny droplets of chemical into the air where they are widely distributed and easily inhaled. If there is an alternative to a product packed in an aerosol can, insist on using it. Keep lids on glues and other volatile items when not in use and work with them only when absolutely necessary while ensuring that the area is as well ventilated as possible. To cut down your exposure to **formaldehyde** place one or two spider plants on your desk if there is room, or at least on a window sill close to you. Spider plants and other house plants absorb formaldehyde from indoor air (see Chapter 3 for more details).

If you work at a VDU fit a protective screen (see Chapter 6). An ionizer or torch cactus (see p.179) positioned close to the screen will help to reduce static and positive ions (see Chapters 6 and 8).

✖ Perfume departments

There are over 40 different chemicals used to make perfumes, and allergic reactions can occur even if the perfume is not being worn. Sometimes just being close to someone who is wearing a perfume formulated with a chemical you are sensitive to is enough to cause running eyes, headache or mood change.

Cut the risks
Taking vitamin C regularly can help to reduce some allergic reactions, but the best defence is to find out exactly which perfumes do affect you and avoid them wherever possible. If perfume counters make you feel unwell, avoid them and find a

natural scent. The Body Shop sells perfume oils containing natural essences plus some synthetic ingredients. If these do not suit you, contact Neal's Yard Pharmacy in Covent Garden, London, as they sell all-natural perfume oils.

✖ Petrol stations and exhaust fumes

Filling a car up with petrol releases volatile chemicals including tetraethyl **lead**, 1,2-dibromethane and aromatic compounds like the solvent **benzene**. Exhaust fumes contain many toxic chemicals including **carbon monoxide**.

Cut the risks
When filling a vehicle with petrol, avoid inhaling the vapours. Vitamin C detoxifies the body and, if vapours have been accidentally inhaled, it can reduce symptoms like headache and nausea. 250 to 750 mg is the recommended dosage.

Exhaust fumes are heavier at the back of a car or bus and are made worse by opening windows. A parked car continues to emit exhaust fumes until the engine completely cools down and is best parked outside if the garage is under inhabited rooms.

✖ Print and copy shops

Printer's ink contains numerous chemicals including **ammonia**, **formaldehyde**, **naphtha**, **phenol**, **toluene** and **xylene**. Photocopiers release **ozone**, **carbon monoxide**, **selenium**, **ammonium**, nitrogen oxides including **nitrogen dioxide**, electrostatic charges and high levels of positive ions. Chemicals from slow-drying inks can be an unsuspected source of potentially allergenic chemicals. Photocopiers release several chemicals – see under Offices (above) for more information.

Cut the risks
Feeling ill while waiting in a printer's is probably indicative of a sensitivity to the chemicals found in printer's ink. Your health may also be affected, but more subtly, by books at home or at work. Keep bookshelves out of your bedroom and living room or any other room where you tend to spend much time and put

some large spider plants in your office if you have to keep books there. (See Chapter 3 for more details of plants' ability to remove pollutants from indoor air.)

✖ TV and electrical appliance showrooms

Electrical items like TVs, videos, stereo systems, computers and so on create unhealthy levels of positive ions in the air and electromagnetic radiation. Carpets, chipboard and plywood shelving contribute to **formaldehyde** levels in the environment, and plastic casings and wiring on electrical equipment give off toxic vapours when warmed. Electrostatic charges also dry the air.

Cut the risks
If you feel unwell in electrical showrooms, it may be necessary to research the product before shopping for it. Read consumers' magazines and consult friends who have similar items. If you are aware of an extreme sensitivity to electrical items, avoid large warehouse-style shops, and if you work in one, persuade the management to install a commercial ionizer by your counter to reduce positive static and revitalize the air. For more information on ionizers see Chapters 3, 6 and 8.

Radiation and Earth Forces

In the eighteenth century, before electricity was discovered, human exposure to electromagnetic radiation came only from the earth (and small amounts from space). In the last fifty years, due to electrical transmission, radar, television and radio, exposure has increased tens of thousands of times. There is now nowhere on earth that is unaffected.

Natural electric and magnetic currents from the earth and space have played a part in human existence since life began. Electro-encephalographs register the human brain operating at between 1 and 20 Hz, which is identical in frequency to the natural electrical waves which surround the earth – alternating extremely low frequency resonances known as Schumann waves. These are believed to control biological timing mechanisms, and blocking them can disrupt human brain patterns.

Since the mid-1940s, man-made electromagnetic frequencies – radar, telephones, microwaves, radio, television and electrical transmission – have been steadily expanding. Our global society now runs on electromagnetic energy and there is nowhere left unaffected by it. Even in the most remote mountain valleys there are power frequencies of 50 or 60 Hz as well as shortwave radio waves. In the late 1970s, scientists discovered that outputs from power distribution systems in North America are affecting part of the atmosphere which dominates the earth's magnetic field, the magnetosphere. How this will ultimately affect either the human race or the earth's ecology is presently unknown.

The electromagnetic spectrum ranges from extremely low frequencies like those generated by power lines to the high frequencies of gamma rays and nuclear fallout. Wavelengths within this spectrum are categorized as either non-ionizing or ionizing radiation. The distinguishing factor between the two is their frequency. Radioactive materials capable of causing damage to cell nuclei are known as ionizing radiation and have frequencies over 3000,000,000 Hz. X-rays, alpha, beta and gamma rays, radon, nuclear radiation and fallout, ultraviolet light (which is on the border of the X-ray region) and cosmic rays are all forms of ionizing radiation. The very high frequencies are capable of splitting an electron from its atom.

Non-ionizing radiation (NIR) is of a lesser frequency at the lower end of the electromagnetic scale – the cut-off point between the two occurs in the ultraviolet region of the visible light spectrum. Some NIR is extremely low frequency, like that emitted by powerlines or the extra low frequencies now used to track submarines. Slightly higher up the scale are navigation radio, radio waves, microwaves, radar and TV. VDUs emit frequencies from the lower, middle and higher parts of the spectrum.

Every human thought, emotion and action is initiated by an electrical impulse 'firing' a nerve cell. Microelectrical currents are vital to the brain and body's functions, and artificial electrical fields can disturb these delicate signalling systems. High-level exposure to geopathic zones (disturbances in the earth's natural electromagnetic field) or to man-made electromagnetic fields may compromise the body's intricate electromagnetic balance, resulting in a disruption of biological processes such as communication amongst cells, white blood cell activity and the function of the immune system. Scientists have already tentatively connected diseases like leukaemia with ultra-high exposure to extremely low electromagnetic frequencies (ELFs) such as those from high tension powerlines.

Some of the first evidence that electromagnetic fields could cause health problems came from Russian research in the 1960s and early 1970s which was triggered by the high incidence of illness amongst electrical switchyard workers – there is now a standard for public exposure to powerline frequencies one thousand times lower than that considered safe in Western countries. In the USA it is illegal to build a house within 350–375 feet of a high voltage powerline.

> From 1953–1976 the Russians irradiated the United States Embassy in Moscow with varying electromagnetic frequencies. The three Ambassadors serving there during this time died of cancer.

Researchers attempting to establish the effects of electromagnetic frequencies (EMFs) on the body have put forward a number of theories. Some frequencies and strengths of extremely low frequency waves (ELFs), especially those in the 50–60 Hz range, can alter the brain tissue's release of calcium. Another avenue of research found that ELF fields encourage higher production of a particular enzyme in mouse, rat and human cancer cells. This indicates that ELFs could encourage cancerous growth, but not necessarily cause it.

Exposure to certain levels of electromagnetic energy can also speed or assist healing. Just as the negative aspects of electromagnetic waves are only recently being investigated, so too are its positive aspects. Doctors know that the application of small currents of electricity can speed up bone healing, and some acupuncturists stimulate the flow of energy in the body by using electro-acupuncture, either through the needles or by placing a probe over precise meridians. There are several other electro-medical techniques under investigation.

ELECTROMAGNETIC FIELDS

The fields from domestic appliances decrease rapidly within a short distance and there is disagreement about whether they can significantly affect health. However, more and more evidence is emerging that they may. Canadian researchers found that pregnant women sleeping with electric blankets turned on had longer pregnancies and a higher percentage of miscarriages than normal; and there is continuing disagreement about the dangers, if any, associated with computer visual display units, VDUs.

In order to place the VDU argument into perspective it is necessary to understand a little about how a television functions. TVs emit a very small amount of ionizing radiation from the screen as X-rays, but the main source of non-ionizing electromagnetic radiation comes from the entire unit. A television will emit a variety of frequencies from the 50 Hz power frequency to radio frequencies in the MHz range. The picture comprises separate horizontal lines generated from left to right (the raster sweep) and contains a 'fly-back' circuit which returns the line sweep to the left side of the screen at the end of each line. This circuit operates at a very low frequency range and is a major part of the frequencies given off. The electromagnetic field is generated within the circuitry of the set, rather than the screen as is commonly believed, but because the size of the screen determines the power at which the circuits work, the larger the screen, the stronger and more radiating the fields.

The pattern of radiation from a VDU is similar to that from a TV, although models produced after 1982 are likely to emit weaker broadband radiation than older models; this was limited after computers were found to be interfering with airport control towers.

The hazards of using a VDU differ from those of the TV in that operators have to sit much closer, and in office situations numerous computers may be in use at once, multiplying the danger of irradiation from the sides and backs of adjacent machines. In 1987 a World Health Organization panel endorsed a Canadian report that VDU operators should not work within one metre of the rear or sides of nearby terminals unless they had been tested to emit only low levels of NIR. The EEC is now taking similar action which may come into effect in the UK at the beginning of 1991.

Guidelines for General Safety

☐ Sit at least 5 to 10 feet away from the television screen – EMR 'drops off' at a distance. Frequencies travel through walls and building materials, and for this reason a TV should never be located against an interior wall if this is possible. Never locate a baby's cot against a wall where a TV backs on to it.

☐ Californian research confirms that pregnant women using VDU terminals for more than 20 hours a week have a 40 per cent increased incidence of miscarriage compared with non-users. Protect yourself by sitting 30 inches back from the screen – this reduces the level of electromagnetic radiation you will be exposed to. Take regular breaks, fit a screen which will reduce the electromagnetic radiation in the higher radiofrequency range by almost 100 percent (none at present protect against the 50 Hz power field), install full spectrum lights (see Chapters 3 and 8 for more details), and use an ionizer close to the screen. Next time you are in the market for a computer, consider a laptop with an LCD screen. LCDs do not contain the cathode ray tube found in TVs and VDUs and do not generate the same type or degree of EMFs.

☐ The torch cactus (*Cereus peruvianus*), column-like in appearance, can be used as a low tech alternative to an ionizer to counteract the fatigue and headaches sometimes experienced by people who work long hours in front of a VDU or are exposed to electronic equipment at close range. This discovery is being utilized by workers on the New York Stock Exchange to restore equilibrium to the electromagnetically disturbed environment and has equal potential in any area where electronic equipment is being used.

☐ Use a battery operated clock/radio by your bed as these do not generate the 50 Hz frequencies emitted by mains electric appliances. Sleeping next to a mains-run appliance exposes you to several uninterrupted hours of EMFs.

☐ If you use an electric blanket, switch it off at the mains before getting into bed.

☐ In the bedroom, switch off all electrical appliances at the mains before going to sleep.

☐ Have microwave door seals checked regularly and never allow children to look through the door when the oven is operating

☐ It may be wise to limit your use of cordless telephones – these devices communicate by generating an electromagnetic field; the same EMF has been found to be present in the brain when the transmit button is pressed. There have been no studies carried out, at the time of writing, to test whether extensive use of these phones has any negative effects on health.

☐ Turn electrical appliances off at the mains when not in use.

☐ Busch Masheder Associates, architects of the Green Home (see Chapter 8), have devised an electrical layout for the home which reduces exposure to EMFs and minimizes cumulative exposure to 50 Hz frequencies.

☐ If moving home, check that you do not move into a house located close to overhead power lines.

☐ It is possible to measure the electric fields generated by some household appliances using a small battery operated AM radio. The radio will respond only to electrical frequencies, not magnetic fields, but this will still give a reasonable idea of the EMF field emitted. It will give a rough idea of the levels of non-ionizing radiation generated by items which emit radio frequencies: computers, TVs, stereos etc. Electric ovens or hair dryers will not register.

To measure the EMF field of an appliance (the TV is probably the best item to start with), turn the AM radio on, tune to a place where no station is audible and turn the volume to maximum. Hold the radio about 12 inches away from the front of the appliance and switch it on. As you move away the 'noise' level will diminish and then stop. At the point where it stops, the non-ionizing radiation level likely to reach you is minimal.

GEOPATHIC STRESS

The Chinese have long believed that Yin and Yang extend to natural earth forces and employ Feng Shui, geomancers, to advise on the siting of new buildings. Other ancient civilizations also took the precaution of employing geomancers to ensure that they sited their buildings on favourable areas. These precautions were not based on superstition or tradition; the earth does emit radiations. In fact, this magnetic field is believed to be utilized by many animals and fish; examples are the homing instinct of pigeons and the migratory patterns of birds. Ancient stone circles, monuments and ley lines have been associated with unusual magnetic forces emanating from the earth and appear to have a polarity which interacts with the human body and mind.

Around the time of the fourteenth century, the medical profession joined with the Church to persecute dowsers for practising witchcraft. This led to a decline in knowledge about earth 'forces' for four centuries. Today, interest in the phenomenon of earth radiations is being re-explored, and both the German and Polish governments have funded major research projects into the health effects on humans of areas of disrupted magnetic earth radiations known as geopathic stress zones.

A geopathic stress zone is an area where the earth's natural wavelengths have become distorted by underground water, crossing underground streams, fault lines, caverns or certain mineral deposits. Much evidence is accumulating which shows that these fluctuating radiations can have a detrimental effect on health, especially when they occur in areas where we spend a large proportion of our time – the bedroom or office for example. German research has linked the incidence of serious disease, including cancer, with spending long periods of time in geopathically stressed zones in a home built on a 'stressed' area and some traffic accident 'black spots' have been found located close to a geopathically stressed area – the Russians are conducting research into this phenomenon too. The rays are said to be strongest at night and during a thunderstorm.

In England, Dr Rolf Gordon has researched into geopathic stress and has made some interesting observations about 'stressed' areas. In his book *Are You Sleeping in a Safe Place?* (available from the Dulwich Health Society), he observes that dogs will not sleep in areas over disrupted earth rays, and several other animals also avoid areas of geopathic disturbance.

How do you know if you are being exposed to geopathic stress?

☐ Do you suffer from any of the following vague symptoms, unrelated to a diagnosed medical condition: regular poor sleep, fatigue, pallor, irritability, depression, lack of appetite, poor concentration? If several of these symptoms apply to you or family members, and aspects of lifestyle are not obviously contributing to them, the Dulwich Health Society (address opposite) may be able to shed some light on them for you, or at least give you an avenue of investigation to follow. There appears to be a possible correlation between infertility in either men or women sleeping over geopathically stressed zones.

☐ Do your children suffer from any of the following symptoms, unrelated to a diagnosed medical condition: tiredness, lack of appetite in the morning, moodiness, lack of concentration, depression, slow learning or hyperactivity, aggressiveness, poor sleeping, nightmares, moving to the edges or ends of the bed to sleep? If several of these symptoms are obvious, and no other medical explanation can be found, it would be worth contacting the Dulwich Health Society (address opposite) for information about geopathic stress.

☐ If you believe that your home may contain areas of geopathic stress, or if you are interested in finding out whether there may be stress zones running through areas where you spend several hours a day, follow the instructions outlined in *Are You Sleeping in a Safe Place?* or contact the British Society of Dowsers (address opposite) to have your home dowsed for geopathic stress zones.

☐ Your bed should be moved to a 'safe' area if it is found to be crossed by geopathic stress lines (the whole of a bed with a metal base or springs, or a water bed will be affected). This should be done very gradually in cases of heart conditions. Moving the bed out of a geopathic zone may result in temporary worsening of health conditions, but these will disappear quickly.

Contacts:

The Dulwich Health Society,
130 Gypsy Hill,
London,
SE19 1PL

The British Society of Dowsers,
Sycamore Cottage,
Tamley Lane,
Hastingleigh,
Ashford,
Kent,
TN25 5HW
Telephone (0233) 75 253

IONIZING RADIATION

Many of the dangers to health posed by ionizing radiation are well known, although in the recent past X-rays and radioactivity were considered to be almost harmless because of the time lapse between radiation exposure and effects on health. In 1896 Thomas Edison gave the first public display of X-rays using his Fluoroscope machine – and started a trend which for the next few decades would lead to tens of thousands of people being exposed to dangerous levels of radiation. In the 1920s girls painted luminous numbers on watch dials with radioactive paint, radium water was sold as a health drink, schizophrenics were injected with radioactive materials, beauty salons used X-rays to remove unwanted hair, women's ovaries were irradiated as a treatment for depression, and hundreds of commercial gimmicks appeared based on X-rays.

Ionizing radiation is now the most strictly controlled material in the world, but there are aspects of its effects on the human body which are still unknown, especially those involving genetics, diseases other than cancer, and its potential to affect the human body at very low doses. Eighty-five percent of our daily exposure to radiation comes from natural sources such as cosmic rays and decay products from certain rocks and soils. Air travel exposes people to higher levels of radiation due to the increased proximity to cosmic rays. Exposure to artificial sources includes nuclear fallout from accidents like Chernobyl, nuclear weapons testing, and particularly medical X-rays. Minute amounts also reach us from luminous clock and watch dials – new ones are luminesced with tritium or promethum 147 which emit lower levels of radiation than the old materials – smoke alarms containing americium-241, satellite dishes, TV sets, VDUs, gun sights, lit telephone dials, exit signs, record anti-static brushes and camping gas mantles. We are even exposed to radiation from tobacco smoke, and porcelain false teeth are given their shine by the addition of uranium to the base compounds.

Ionizing radiation causes damage by smashing molecules to pieces and producing free radicals. These oxidants are highly reactive and disrupt normal cell metabolism. Certain nutrients act as anti-oxidants in the body and protect cells, and numerous foods can prevent the uptake of radioactive materials, while others cause their harmless excretion. For more information on free radicals, antioxidants, and radiation protection see Chapter 7.

RADON

People in certain parts of the country, especially Devon and Cornwall, may be exposed to radon from soil and rocks. Radon comes from the radioactive decay of uranium which is particularly prevalent in granite. It rises from soil and rocks, mixes with the air and is diluted in the atmosphere unless it seeps into a building, becomes trapped and concentrates in the internal environment. This is most likely to occur when draught-proofing methods have been utilized. Radon decay results in the formation of minute particles known as radon 'daughters' or decay products. These can attach to dust in the environment and may be inhaled where they deposit in the lungs and emit radiation, therefore increasing the risk of developing lung cancer.

The following chart gives a sense of proportion to the sources of ionizing radiation. As you can see, natural radiation accounts for the greatest percentage:

Chart 6.1 Sources of ionizing radiation

Sources of Ionizing Radiation	Approximate Percentage
Radon and thoron from the ground, soil and rocks	47
Gamma rays from the ground and from buildings	14
Food and drink	12
Cosmic rays	14
Artificial radiation, including medical irradiation, fallout from weapons testing, occupational exposure and consumer products	13

Figures taken from NRPB brochures: '*Radiation Doses – Maps and Magnitudes and Living with Radiation*'

There is no need for concern about radon levels in your home unless you live in certain areas of Devon or Cornwall, the Derbyshire Dales, Deeside or Somerset. If you would like more information about these areas, send general enquiries accompanied by an SAE to The Information Officer, National Radiological Protection Board, Chilton, Didcot, Oxon, OX11 0RQ, Telephone Abingdon (0235) 831600. If you suspect that you might be living in a hotspot and would like more information about your risk, write to the same address but send it to NRPB Radon Survey. You will be sent a short questionnaire, and on the basis of the answers the NRPB will advise you as to whether the level of radon could require monitoring.

SMOKE ALARMS

There are two types of smoke detector: ionization and photo-electric. The ionization type contain a tiny piece of radioactive americium-241 which ionizes the air within a chamber and creates a constant electric current between two electrodes. When smoke enters the detector and disrupts the current it triggers an alarm. Photoelectric devices contain a beam of light that strikes a light-sensitive photocell in a chamber. Smoke disrupting the beam sets off the alarm.

Older photoelectric detectors were slower than the ionizing type, but the new models are comparable; in fact a summary in the American consumer magazine, *Consumer Reports*, rates photoelectric smoke alarms faster than ionization units for detecting slow smouldering fires, and only three seconds behind the ionizing units for blazing fires. The drawback is that photoelectric cell detectors are more expensive and harder to find, but it is worth the investment and added effort, not necessarily because the exposure level is likely to be a danger, but because disposal of the ionization type involves exposing the environment to one of the longest-term decaying radioactive materials.

Nutritional Self-Defence

We still have some control over the food we eat and the water we drink, but the air we breathe is a different matter.

Over thousands of years we have adapted to the natural toxicants in the environment and foods, but within the last five decades the volume and variety of synthetic chemicals has increased so fast that we have had little chance to build up our defences and still less to understand or predict their systemic effects or study their combined impact on the body.

It is not possible to establish a natural immunity to chemical exposure as one can to viruses or bacteria; in fact chemicals frequently become more harmful as the body attempts to process them – for example, detoxification of some hydrocarbons forms new and more dangerous chemicals. But you can make your body more tolerant of toxic substances by increasing its ability to excrete and neutralize them and counter cell-damaging free oxygen radicals.

ABOUT FREE RADICALS

Chemical substances known as free oxygen radicals or superoxides are released as part of the body's immune defence system and as by-products of chemical reactions in the cells. They are formed by oxygen molecules and have an extra electron which makes them highly reactive and unstable; consequently they are devoted to combining with other molecules in order to complete themselves. This is what makes them efficient within the immune system, but if their numbers get out of control their actions can result in cellular damage.

Free radicals get out of control as a result of exposure to certain pollutants, chemicals and ionizing radiation; they then become a danger to the body rather than its defender, and may combine with cell membranes, enzymes and even the genetic material in the cell nucleus. In this instance they damage host cells by pulling electrons away from their molecules. This is known as oxidation, and results in many aspects of cell organization being affected. It is also possible that genetic information may be distorted because the living blueprints that tell each cell how to function and reproduce are sabotaged. This can disrupt the regulation of cell division so that cells divide uncontrollably and generate the possibility of malignant cell changes, tumours or cancerous growth. Free radicals are also known to be involved in the initiation of diseases like cardiovascular disorders and premature aging.

That chemicals and pollutants are involved in the initiation of cancer and toxic damage is true, but this is brought about by the free radical form of a toxic chemical, not the parent molecule itself. The chemicals we eat, breathe and absorb undergo many complex changes in the body. They may be transformed into several other chemicals or converted by enzymes into a new molecular form – free radicals or superoxides.

There are many ways in which the balance of free radicals in our bodies can be upset. For instance, inhaling tobacco smoke liberates billions of free radicals into the blood. In fact, any combustion process creates free radicals. Heavy metals are toxic, but their free radical derivatives are even more dangerous. Chemicals we encounter in smog – formaldehyde, acetaldehyde and acrolein – are easily converted to free radicals, and carbon tetrachloride (CTC), a potent liver carcinogen, has been shown to cause cancer when it is converted into its free radical form. This is also true of many environmental toxicants and pollutants including chlorine, ozone and radiation. Several food constituents increase the production of free radicals – among those implicated are rancid and heated (particularly unsaturated) fats, burned, irradiated or mouldy foods, and heated proteins.

ABOUT THE IMMUNE SYSTEM

The multiplication of free radicals as well as causing cell damage also impairs immunity. Cumulative and continued exposure to free radical-producing chemicals can weaken the body's defences, making it more vulnerable to viral infection. Opportunistic infections such as candida, or conditions such as M.E. ('yuppie flu'), are becoming more common because of the immune system's decreased ability to respond appropriately to challenge.

A clue to this emerged from the mysterious illness suffered by grey seals in the North Sea. The seals' low resistance to the viral epidemic appears to be inextricably linked with over-exposure to chemical pollutants that work their way up through the food chain. Many persistent chemicals are dumped into the sea, and PCBs (polychlorinated biphenyls) particularly have a tendency to accumulate in fatty tissue. Seals have a layer of blubber that can harbour considerable quantities of fat soluble chemicals. PCBs damage the glandular system and interfere with liver function, and the combination of this with exposure to numerous other chemicals is believed to have precipitated the deaths by weakening the immune system.

Allergies, too, are associated with a weakened immune system; some people feel unwell when exposed to chemicals in the home, petrol fumes or vehicle exhaust. Every person has a fluctuating tolerance level which is influenced by the quality of sleep, nutrition, exercise, and also by stress levels and exposure to infectious organisms. If the body is in a weakened state, even minimal exposure to chemicals can be sufficient to precipitate an allergic reaction. Therapeutic doses of selenium have been administered in medical trials to people with extreme chemical sensitivities and has often resulted in improvement. This indicates that chemical sensitivity, in addition to other negative effects of toxic chemicals, is caused by the production of free radicals from toxic chemical exposure, and the individual's inability to handle the effects of elevated levels of free radicals.

HOW TO AVOID THE AVOIDABLE

We still have some control over the quality of the food we eat and the water we drink, but the air we breathe is a different matter. Towns, cities and busy roads are the kinds of environment where every breath contains a wide range of pollutants which are carried to every part of the body in the bloodstream. To help the body deal with this daily assault, avoidable pollutants and chemicals should be kept to a minimum.

> The lighter the body's avoidable chemical load, the better it can deal with the unavoidable pollutants.

☐ Choose organically grown produce, naturally reared, antibiotic and growth-hormone-free meats, and free range chicken and eggs whenever possible. They are far less likely to be contaminated with chemicals than their commercially grown or battery counterparts.

If organically grown produce is not available, wash and soak fruit and vegetables in a solution of warm water and distilled vinegar for 5 minutes. The vinegar will acidify the water and remove up to 85 percent of the surface chemical pesticide residues. It is impossible to remove most of the chemicals since many insecticides act systemically, which means that they are taken up by the whole plant into the cells. The skins of unwrapped fruit and vegetables may be contaminated with lead, especially when purchased from stalls close to traffic.

Choosing the majority of your fruit and vegetables from those in season cuts down the risks of exposure to the chemicals used to delay ripening, preserve colour and prolong shelf life.

☐ Remove fat from cuts of meat, because in addition to the negative effects of saturated fat, this is where numerous chemicals, pesticides and toxicants accumulate. Limit intake of fatty dairy foods such as butter, cream, and cheese as they may also contain chemical residues. Low-fat or goat milk dairy products are a healthier substitute.

☐ Use filtered or spring water for cooking and drinking. A good water filter is well worth the initial investment (see Chapter 8) as the UK's water in many areas exceeds the EEC's maximum admissible concentration of **lead**, **aluminium sulphate**, nitrates and pesticides and may also contain excessive levels of trihalo-methanes – potentially cancer-causing chemicals formed when water containing organic matter such as sewage is treated with chlorine. Chlorine itself is a potent chemical which has been implicated in heart disease.

☐ Significant sources of aluminium include 'silver' foil for packing and storing food, yogurt lids, some antiperspirants, baking powder, tea, drink cans, food additives E173 (silver food colour now withdrawn but may still be found in old stock), E554, E556, E541, aluminium hydroxide antacids, soy-based baby formulas, and aluminium sulphate used to clarify drinking water in peaty areas. Aluminium cookware can be a major source of contamination, especially when acid foods such as tomatoes and citrus fruits are cooked in them. Stainless steel or glass cookware will not contaminate food. There may be a danger of cadmium contamination from damaged enamel cookware, especially if it is red or orange.

☐ Processed foods contain chemical preservatives, additives, colours and flavourings which the body has to detoxify, but some food additives are healthy. E101 is vitamin B_2 used as a food colouring; E160 is a carotene (vitamin A) used as a food colouring; E300–E304 are ascorbic acid (vitamin C) used as antioxidants to preserve food; E306–9 are tocopherol (vitamin E) antioxidants used to preserve food; E322 is lecithin and is used as an emulsifier; E375 is vitamin B_3 used as a stabilizer; E440 is pectin used as a gelling agent.

☐ Decrease dietary intake of free radicals by limiting fried, burned, smoked or barbecued foods, rancid nuts, seeds and vegetable oils. Check bags of nuts and seeds for those which appear yellow/

orange. These are rancid and should be discarded. Wheatgerm becomes rancid very rapidly due to its high wheatgerm oil content. To prevent the consumption of rancid oils, buy only fresh, vacuum-packed wheatgerm, refrigerate it when open and consume within 1 week. Refrigerate all vegetable oils.

☐ Fish caught off the British coast are likely to be contaminated with chemical pollutants dumped in the sea; Dover sole should be particularly avoided for this reason. Frozen fish may have been treated with preservative chemicals, so it is important to check labels, but much of it comes from the less polluted Arctic Ocean or the far reaches of the North Sea. Avoid shellfish as they scavenge for food on the bottom of the ocean and ingest high levels of chemicals.

☐ A diet high in refined sugar decreases the function of the immune system and affects the body's ability to cope with toxicants and pollutants. Pure uncooked honey, molasses, and concentrated fruit juice from organically grown fruit make acceptable substitutes.

☐ Exercising near heavy traffic or city streets increases toxic chemical ingestion as a result of raised metabolism and deeper breathing. In 1989, hot weather brought the worst air pollution in London and the south east since 1976. The British Lung Foundation produced anti-smog masks and warned that more than two hours spent outside without them could permanently damage the lungs. In London, levels of surface ozone exceeded WHO safe guidelines by between 12 and 35 percent. Britain regularly exceeds WHO safe guidelines for **sulphur dioxide**, particulates (e.g. diesel smut), **nitrogen dioxide** and **carbon monoxide** as well. The lead, carbon monoxide and general pollution level in cities is highest during overcast days and lowest on clear days after rain. Ozone levels are highest on hot, sunny days. (See under *ozone* and *carbon monoxide* in Chapter 2 for more details.)

☐ Excessive use of drugs, especially over-the-counter preparations, stresses the liver and kidneys. For more information on prescription drugs, their interaction with nutrients, and alternative natural remedies see *The Medicine Chest* (Thorsons, 1988).

Breaking the Coffee Habit

Coffee, tea, colas, chocolate and cocoa all contain caffeine. Coffee also contains numerous other chemicals, including methylxanthines which are toxic. Coffee beans tend to have high levels of pesticide residues, and non-water-decaffeinated coffee is often treated with the same chemical used in dry-cleaning solvents: methylene chloride. If you wish to cut down or stop drinking caffeinated coffee, it should be done over a period of time. Two to four cups of strong coffee contain enough caffeine to stimulate the adrenal glands, increase the production of adrenalin and increase the heart rate and metabolism. In time the body begins to rely on the shot of caffeine to 'wake up', and if caffeine is stopped suddenly, numerous withdrawal symptoms can occur including shaking, depression, temper, weepiness and difficulty dealing with stressful situations. To gradually decrease or stop coffee use the following approach:

Weeks One to Four
Use a quarter of a teaspoon less of your regular coffee and replace it with a quarter of a teaspoon of grain or dandelion coffee substitute. Continue this for four weeks until your body becomes used to the decreased level of caffeine, and you become accustomed to the taste.

Weeks Four to Eight
Cut the regular coffee down to half a teaspoon and add half a teaspoon of coffee substitute. Continue this for four weeks.

Week Eight
Reduce the regular coffee to a quarter of a teaspoon and add three quarters of a teaspoon of coffee substitute. Continue with this combination until you feel able to switch entirely to coffee substitute.

Tea can be reduced quite easily by substituting one or two daily cups of regular tea with rooibosch (red bush tea) or a herbal mixture that you enjoy.

Breaking the Smoking Habit

> Each inhalation of cigarette smoke contains 1000 billion droplets of tar. In these droplets and the gases surrounding them are over 3000 different chemicals including cadmium, carbon monoxide, benzopyrenes, ammonia and aldehydes, besides nicotine which is one of the most toxic and addicting of all poisons.

For help with giving up smoking contact ASH (see Chapter 8 under 'Health Groups' p.241). Giving up can be aided by the following plan for nutritional support which will help to detoxify the body and decrease the addictive and withdrawal effects of nicotine.

If you are taking prescribed medicines, check with your doctor before attempting to take high doses of vitamins or minerals. Vitamin C can interact with numerous drugs, and this programme should not be attempted if any of the drugs being taken are listed under Vitamin C on p.214.

One Week Before Giving Up

Eat lightly and increase the intake of fresh vegetables and fruit. Drink plenty of still mineral/spring water. Decrease consumption of alcohol, coffee and tea. Take the following supplements:

Supplement	Breakfast	Lunch	Supper	Bed
Vitamin C 250 mg with bioflavonoids	1	1	1	1
Vitamin B complex 50 mg	1	1		
GTF chromium 200 mcg	1		1*	
Multiple mineral (high potency)				2

*The extra GTF should be added after the second day and then continued.

The Day You Stop, and for a Week After

Supplement	Breakfast	Lunch	Supper	Bed
Vitamin C 500 mg* with bioflavonoids	2	2	2	2
Vitamin B complex 50 mg[†] (time release)	1	1		
GTF chromium 200 mcg (non-time release)	1	1		
Pantothenic acid (B$_5$) 250 mg	1	1		
Multiple mineral (high potency)	2			2

The Week After and Beyond

Over the next week gradually decrease the vitamin C and GTF to half, but continue with the same level of B complex, B$_5$ and multiple minerals.

The following week, and until you feel you can do without it, continue with approximately 1000 mg of vitamin C and 50–100 mg of vitamin B complex a day, and with the night-time multiple minerals. Cut the GTF chromium down to 200 mcg in the morning with breakfast, and the B$_5$ down to 250 mg in the afternoon with lunch.

It is believed that eating sunflower seeds provokes the release of chemicals in the body similar to those provoked by smoking, so you might find it helpful to eat them frequently as a snack, or whenever the desire to smoke arises.

*Everyone's threshold for vitamin C differs. When tolerance has been reached, the bowels may become loose and this may happen with smaller doses than those suggested in the programme. To find your optimum level, cut back the vitamin C by small quantities until intestinal normality is regained.

[†]Taking high potency vitamin B complex supplements will colour the urine bright yellow. This is an effect of vitamin B$_2$ and is harmless.

HOW TO DETOXIFY THE UNAVOIDABLE

We are equipped with mechanisms for detoxifying many harmful substances, but because of escalating exposure to unavoidable chemicals and pollutants these mechanisms are becoming increasingly overloaded. This causes toxicants to become distributed throughout the body in cells, tissue and fluids. Their presence precipitates a vicious circle which results in the retention of more toxicants, reduces the capacity of the eliminative process still further, and subsequently decreases the body's ability to eliminate them. Similarly, a diet that is too high in fats, proteins, sodium, refined sugars and other refined foods reduces this natural capacity.

Through detoxification the cycle is broken, and concentration of wastes in the body can be reduced to a non-toxic level. However, this should be done slowly and with nutritional support, because when the total body burden of pollutants exceeds our ability to detoxify, these substances are integrated into bone, fat, brain and other tissue. A rapid cleansing programme, or even rapid weight loss, liberates stored toxicants too quickly, because as fat is used for energy, a flood of them is released into the blood, and when calcium is released from the bones for normal body functions, so are toxicants: toxicants that ultimately affect the immune and nervous systems, brain, liver, kidneys, and other vital organs.

TEN-DAY DETOX PROGRAMME

The detoxification programme which follows is aimed at decreasing the number of toxic agents in the diet and increasing the efficiency of the digestion and organs of elimination. The body's detoxification mechanisms are greatly enhanced by an optimum intake of essential nutrients: vitamins and minerals, essential fatty acids and protein. Chlorella is suggested as the source of these as its nutrients are easily assimilated and the high chlorophyll content and special cell walls detoxify and eliminate heavy metals and toxicants.

Live and unprocessed foods add bulk to the diet and speed up the intestinal transit time, carrying waste efficiently through the body, and mineral and spring water aid the kidneys in detoxification. Raw vegetable juices are an excellent source of enzymes and minerals, especially potassium, which stimulates good digestion and elimination. For more information about Chlorella, including how to obtain it, see later (page 230).

As the body detoxifies, it is normal to feel tired, so any fasting or detoxification regimen is best undertaken at a time when it is possible to rest. Exercise is important after the first day, but it must be gentle and preferably in the fresh air. *A doctor should be consulted about the possibility of using a detoxification diet by people who are underweight, diabetic or have a serious medical condition, or by those taking prescribed medicines on a regular basis.* Those taking a short course of medicine may begin the detoxification diet when the course is finished.

Day One
Avoid food and instead drink frequent glasses of fresh vegetable juice made from 2–3 large carrots, 1–2 sticks of celery and a slice of raw beetroot. If you do not have a vegetable juicer, fast, but drink plenty of still mineral or spring water. Take Chlorella as directed on the package. A day of liquids only will give your digestive system a rest and begin to flush out toxicants.

Day Two

Eat organic fruit such as grapes, pears, apples, and oranges. Drink spring or still mineral water with a squeeze of fresh lemon juice, or organic fruit juices, especially cherry or grape. Take Chlorella as directed on the package.

Day Three

Drink frequent small glasses of fresh vegetable juice and/or spring or still mineral water. Also include herbal tea – chamomile, peppermint, lemon balm, nettle, dandelion root, red clover. Eat steamed root vegetables such as carrots, parsnips and beetroot, and raw salad vegetables including watercress, radishes, garlic, onions, cabbage, and fresh dandelion leaves from an unpolluted source. Take Chlorella as directed on the package.

If garlic and your social life are compatible, it can be taken for one day to aid detoxification. Provided you are not allergic to it, garlic works safely to detoxify heavy metals and clear catarrh from the lungs and digestive system:

1. Chop a clove of fresh garlic into 3 or 4 pieces and swallow it with water. If your digestion is settled, take another clove in the same way an hour later, then another an hour after that.

2. 4 to 6 cloves may be taken in the same way during the evening. This quantity is completely safe, although you may experience temporary bloating of the stomach. Take a bath before going to bed as the garlic will cause toxicants to be released through the skin.

Days Four, Five and Six

Continue with the basic diet (minus the garlic cleanse) outlined in day three and add organically grown brown rice, vegetables (excluding potatoes), and fruit, especially fresh mango, papaya, cherries, pears and apples. Include free-range hormone- and antibiotic-free chicken or turkey and fresh fish such as plaice. Take Chlorella as directed on the package.

Days Seven, Eight and Nine
Add wholemeal buckwheat or rice, pasta, eggs, gluten-free or mixed wholegrain bread/rice cakes, sweet potatoes, and whole grain cereal. Take Chlorella as directed on the package.

Day Ten
Return to a 'normal' diet with plenty of variety but avoid commercially produced red meats, sugar, sweets, cakes, shellfish, coffee, tea and alcohol, and keep consumption of commercial dairy products to a minimum. Make the portions small to begin with as the stomach will have become used to less food. Continue taking Chlorella until the package is finished. If you wish, Chlorella may be continued as part of a regular protective nutritional regimen.

Other Detox Tips

☐ Start each morning with a cup of hot water to which a squeeze of fresh lemon has been added. This wakes up the digestive system and stimulates the liver.

☐ Take regular aerobic exercise such as walking, swimming, rebounding, playing court sports and so on. Exercise mobilizes and eliminates chemical toxicants via increased perspiration and respiration. It also increases oxygen intake and stimulates the lymphatic system to move wastes. Saunas and steam treatments encourage the body to throw off toxicants through the skin.

☐ Use a vegetable fibre skin brush (see page 264, Green Farm Nutrition Centre) to increase circulation and stimulate the skin's ability to eliminate toxicants and remove dead skin cells. Once or twice a day, lay a towel on the floor, stand in the middle and brush the body in circular strokes starting with the feet and progressing upwards. Avoid the breasts, face and neck as the skin is delicate. Shake the towel outside.

PROTECTIVE NUTRITION

Dietary factors are known to minimize absorption of pollutants and a wholesome, varied diet is one of the best defences against potentially harmful chemicals. Certain foods not only enable the body to resist toxicants, but also aid in metabolizing and excreting them. A breakfast of organically grown rolled oats and organic apple juice, for example, speeds up the transit of wastes. Oats and the pectin found in apples are known to assist in the elimination of toxic metals. Certain foods play a role in protecting the body against damage from exposure to radiation.

General Hints

☐ Seaweeds and sea vegetables are a source of iodine which is taken up by the thyroid gland.

> When dietary iodine levels and assimilation are adequate, the thyroid's absorption of radioactive iodine is minimized.

Sodium alginate from seaweeds combines with strontium-90, a breakdown product of radiation, and by acting as a binding agent in the intestine causes its excretion from the body.

☐ Calcium and magnesium bind with radioactive materials and carry them out of the body.

> Sufficient calcium in the bones is known to be protective against radiation and free radical attack.

Good sources of calcium include dairy products, especially cheese and yogurt which are easily digested, canned fish, nuts and pulses, sesame seeds, brewer's yeast, carob, seaweeds, especially hijiki, vegetables, nuts, eggs, oatmeal, fruit and wheatgerm. Sources of magnesium include soy beans, cashews, almonds and brazil nuts, brewer's yeast, wholewheat flour, brown rice, seafoods, bananas, dried fruit, meat and vegetables.

☐ Good sources of organic sodium (not sodium chloride or table/sea salt) include celery, cucumber, dark green leafy vegetables, dandelion leaves, and beetroot.

> Organic sodium is important for the elimination of poisonous substances from the body.

☐ Fresh, preferably organic, fruit and vegetables, wholegrain cereals and pulses are high in fibre.

> Fibre speeds the passage of food through the intestines, so limiting the uptake of harmful chemicals.

☐ Garlic aids in the discharge of heavy metals from the body.

☐ Orange, yellow and dark green vegetables and orange fruit are the main source of beta carotene.

> Carotene protects the lungs against the damaging effects of smoke inhalation, including cancer.

☐ Apples, plums, damsons and bananas are foods high in pectin; pectin is also found in the skins of limes.

> Pectin slows down the intestinal absorption of lead and binds with heavy metals and carries them out of the body.

☐ Adding a teaspoon of virgin olive oil to a daily salad retards the uptake of toxic chemicals by the intestines and aids in their elimination. Other useful oils include sunflower, safflower or grapeseed.

☐ Sulphur prevents the accumulation of waste body toxicants. High sulphur vegetables include garlic, onions, cabbage, radishes, brussels sprouts, kale and mustard greens. Eggs and soy lecithin contain sulphur amino acids which are antioxidant and also bind with heavy metals and carry them out of the body.

It is known that nutrients can help counter free radicals and chemical pollutants. The body has a number of in-built mechanisms which counter free radicals by supplying hydrogen to damaged molecules and preventing them from combining with cell components. These are known as antioxidants and include the enzymes superoxide dismutase, catalase and glutathione peroxidase. A number of dietary factors are precursors of the body's own antioxidants; the key ones are vitamins A, C and E, the minerals selenium, manganese, molybdenum, and zinc, and the amino acids cysteine and taurine. Phosphatidyl choline and methionine, eicosapentaenoic acid (EPA) and beta carotene are also antioxidant. Besides the antioxidant effects, these nutrients stimulate the immune response and are protective against early malignant cell changes.

Research shows that low levels of the vitamins and minerals listed in this chapter increase the body's susceptibility to damage from toxic chemicals, pollutants, radiation, and heavy metals.

VITAMIN A

Vitamin A protects the lungs and the body's cells against the cancer-causing effects of inhaled pollutants.

Beta carotene, the form of vitamin A found in orange and yellow fruit and vegetables, is particularly helpful in protecting the lungs against damage from inhaled pollutants including cigarette smoke, sidestream smoke, and asbestos, all of which are carcinogens, cancer-causing substances. All forms of vitamin A assist in the maintenance of mucous membranes and skin, protecting the body against the damaging effects of pollutants and carcinogens, and increasing immunity to disease. The majority of cancers are those affecting epithelial tissue which lines the external and internal surfaces of the body. Vitamin A is essential for the healthy maintenance of this tissue and is involved in its growth and development, and contributes to the strength and normal reproduction of cells. Loss of cell differentiation is a major feature of cancer, and research has consistently shown that people whose blood levels of this pro-vitamin are adequate have a low risk of developing cancer, especially that of the mouth and lungs.

Beta carotene, pro-vitamin A, acts on both stages of the cancer process – when the cell turns cancerous and when it multiplies. The results of studies indicate that its therapeutic effects may not be due only to its conversion to vitamin A, but that it may also act independently to increase the ability of the immune system to fight infection and the growth of abnormal cells. Its antioxidant effects also act against the damaging effects of oxidising free radicals produced, in part, by exposure to pollutants.

A long-term study by the National Cancer Institute in the USA is centring on the ability of vitamin A to prevent lung cancer in high risk groups. These include heavy smokers and those exposed to asbestos through their occupations. The study is running from 1987 to 1996 and the researchers are optimistic that it will provide information about the prevention of cancer.

How Much Should I Take?

An optimum intake for adults exposed to elevated or constant levels of pollutants in the air could be as high as 5–10,000 iu from fish liver oil, or up to 25,000 iu in the form of beta carotene. An intake of 4.5 mg of beta carotene 3 times a day is recommended as a preventative dose against lung cancer, especially for smokers or those exposed to others' tobacco smoke. Even those who have smoked for many years can reduce their risk of developing lung cancer by daily consuming foods rich in beta carotene. Vitamin A in the form of beta carotene is not toxic, but if taken in excess it may cause a yellow/orange pigmentation of the skin, particularly on the palms of the hands and/or the soles of the feet. This will disappear in a few days once the source of carotene is withdrawn. If a small quantity of carotene produces pigmentation, consult a doctor. If you intend to obtain beta carotene from carrot juice, limit your consumption to approximately 12 oz of juice per day. Carrots, parsnips and a number of other root vegetables, contain a substance that, in excess, suppresses the production of the immune system's white blood cells. Vitamin A in the form of fish liver oil may be toxic to some people in doses above 10,000 iu taken over a period of time. Children up to 5 years should receive their vitamin A naturally from a well planned diet. If a high dose supplement is required consult a doctor or natural practitioner for advice.

If you are taking the Pill or oestrogen, vitamin A should not be used in supplement form as blood levels are already increased, but it is advisable to ensure there is plenty of beta carotene in the diet. Women who are pregnant should avoid vitamin A supplements, concentrating on obtaining this nutrient from a well balanced diet.

What Are the Best Dietary Sources?

Fresh carrot juice provides extra dietary beta carotene. For weaned children, 2 oz mixed with a little spring water will safely increase vitamin A intake. Adults and children over 5 years old can 'supplement' the diet with 6 to 8 oz of fresh carrot juice.

There are two types of vitamin A. Carotene (carotenoids, among which beta carotene, alpha carotene, and gamma carotene are the most biologically active) is found mainly in yellow, orange and green vegetables and fruit and is known as pro-vitamin A. About one sixth of the carotene eaten is converted into the other type, retinol, a usable form called pre-formed vitamin A, in the intestinal tract and is stored in fat tissue throughout the body. The body converts carotene only as needed, eliminating the likelihood of taking too much. Pre-formed vitamin A is found in foods of animal origin.

Sources of vitamin A

Pro-formed Vitamin A	Pre-formed Vitamin A
Carrots	Cod liver oil
Parsley	Halibut liver oil
Spinach	Lamb liver
Turnip tops	Butter
Spring greens	Cheese
Sweet potatoes	Eggs
Watercress	Pre-formed vitamin A is also
Broccoli	added to margarines
Cantaloupe melons	
Endives	
Pumpkin	
Apricots	
Lettuce	
Prunes	
Tomatoes	
Peaches	
Asparagus	

*The foods are listed in descending order of potency

What Decreases My Vitamin A Levels?

Smoking Air pollution	Increase the body's requirements for vitamin A because it is used to protect the cells.
Lipid lowering drugs Tetracyclines	Decrease the body's ability to absorb oily vitamins including vitamin A from fish liver oils and animal products. The absorption of beta carotene is not affected.
Antacids Liquid paraffin	Reduce the absorption of vitamin A, particularly if they are taken regularly.
Penicillins Gout drugs	Decrease the absorption of beta carotene.
Aspirin Paracetamol Alcohol	Regular use/intake depletes the liver's store of vitamin A.

Also: vitamin A levels are reduced by fever, infection, or a diet extremely high in protein.

B COMPLEX VITAMINS

B complex vitamins function as antioxidant co-factors and increase the efficiency of the body's detoxification systems.

Components of the B group of vitamins are involved directly or indirectly in free radical neutralization. They also aid in the release of toxicants, protect against cancerous changes in the cells and are vital for the health of the liver.

Certain dangers from exposure to pollution are decreased by ensuring that intake of all the B group vitamins is sufficient. The body's production of the antioxidant glutathione is dependent on sufficient vitamin B_2 (riboflavin), and B_3 (niacin) is essential in the production of the enzyme NADH and in promoting the release of toxic substances from the tissues. Niacin is being examined by international researchers as a significant link in cancer prevention. At the International Symposium of Niacin Nutrition in 1987 researchers reported that niacin repairs damaged genetic material in cells. Cell mutation can occur during free radical attack and may lead to the genesis of cancerous cell change.

Both vitamin B_5 (pantothenic acid) and B_6 (pyridoxine) are vital co-factors in antioxidant enzyme production, and vitamin B_1 (thiamine) forms a strong team with vitamin C and the amino acid L-cysteine to neutralize free radicals and support the immune system. B_1 also complexes with acetaldehyde found in smoke and smog, and contains sulphur, an important element in the neutralization and excretion of toxicants. B_1 may also prevent the deposition of lead in tissues.

Choline- and methionine-deficient diets have been linked with liver cancer in animals. Choline is manufactured in the body when B_{12} and folic acid are supplied in sufficient quantity, and methionine is present in foods containing all the B group vitamins. B_{12} functions in the detoxification of cyanide found in tobacco smoke.

How Much Should I Take?

An optimum intake for adults exposed to elevated or constant levels of pollutants and stress can range from 25 to 50 mg of vitamin B complex with breakfast and lunch. B complex vitamins are so integrated in function that large doses of any single one may be therapeutically valueless, and may in fact lead to a deficiency of others.

Always take single B vitamins with a complex; for example, if extra B_6 is taken in 50 mg potencies, it is important to accompany it with a supplement containing the complete B complex. B vitamins are not toxic, but if taken singly in large doses a deficit may develop in the others, resulting in symptoms which may be unrecognized as a nutritional imbalance.

Take vitamin C at least two hours apart from vitamin B complex. Ascorbic acid (vitamin C) interferes with B_6 metabolism, and large doses of vitamin C deplete B_{12}. Take ginseng at least 3 hours before or after vitamin C.

Warning

☐ Supplemental vitamin B_1 should only be taken by diabetics under medical supervision.

☐ Supplements of B_2 taken at the same time as the antibiotics erythromycin, lincomycin and tetracycline can decrease their effects.

☐ PABA or folic acid taken with sulphonamide antibiotics may decrease their effects.

☐ Large doses of vitamin B_6 and folic acid can decrease the effectiveness of phenytoin anticonvulsants. Supplemental B_6 also reduces the effectiveness of levodopa anti-parkinsonism drugs.

What Are the Best Dietary Sources?

Rice bran and brewer's yeast are two significant food sources of vitamin B complex. They can be taken with meals to supplement the diet, and are especially good for young children.

B vitamins are easily lost into cooking water during steaming or boiling, but they are not destroyed unless baking soda is added to the cooking water. Vitamin B_2 (riboflavin) is very unstable in light and is converted to lumiflavin which destroys vitamin C. For example, if milk is left on a doorstep in the sun for two hours, ninety percent of its B_2 content will be lost. B_1 is the most unstable of the B vitamins, and is destroyed by sulphur dioxide, a food preservative commonly used in dried fruit. B vitamins are water soluble and are excreted in the urine.

Sources of B complex vitamins

Nutrient	Significant Sources (listed in descending order of potency)
B_1 (Thiamine)	Brewer's yeast Rice bran Wheatgerm Nuts Soya flour Oats/wheat Liver
B_2 (Riboflavin)	Yeast extract/brewer's yeast Liver Wheatgerm Cheese/eggs Meat Soya flour Yogurt/milk Green leafy vegetables Pulses

Nutrient	Significant Sources (listed in descending order of potency)
B$_3$ (Niacin)	Yeast extract/brewer's yeast Nuts Chicken Soya flour Meat Fatty fish Wheat Cheese Dried fruits Wholemeal bread
B$_5$ (Pantothenic acid)	Brewer's yeast/yeast extract Nuts Wheat bran/germ Soya flour Eggs Meat/poultry Oatflakes Pulses Dried fruits Maize Brown rice
B$_6$ (Pyridoxine)	Brewer's yeast Wheat bran Yeast extract Wheatgerm Oatflakes Soya flour Bananas Nuts Meat Fatty fish Brown rice
B$_{12}$ (Cobalamin)	Pig's liver/kidney Fatty fish Meat White fish

Nutrient	Significant Sources (listed in descending order of potency)
B$_{12}$ (Cobalamin) (continued)	Eggs Chicken Cheeses Yogurt Cow's milk
Biotin (Vitamin H) Synthesized by intestinal bacteria	Brewer's yeast/yeast extract Eggs Oatflakes Wheat bran/germ Maize Fatty fish/white fish Meats Brown rice Milk/cheese/yogurt Vegetables
Folic acid (Vitamin M or Bc) Synthesized in the body by intestinal bacteria	Brewer's yeast Soya flour Wheatgerm/bran Nuts Green leafy vegetables Pulses Oatflakes Citrus fruits Eggs Brown rice Fatty fish
Choline and Inositol Choline can be synthesized in the body by the interaction of B$_{12}$ and folic acid with the amino acid methionine. Inositol is synthesized in the body from glucose	Dried liver Lecithin granules Beef heart Egg yolk Liver Steak Wheatgerm Brewer's yeast Oatflakes Nuts and pulses

Nutrient	Significant Sources (listed in descending order of potency)
Choline and Inositol (continued)	Citrus fruits Molasses Pulses Bananas Green leafy vegetables
PABA (para aminobenzoic acid) Can be synthesized in the body by intestinal bacteria	Liver Eggs Molasses Brewer's yeast Wheatgerm

What Decreases My Vitamin B Levels?

Antacids	Deplete B_1, B_2, B_6, B_{12} and folic acid
Antidepressants	Decrease the effects of B_2
Anxiolytics	Deplete B_3, B_5 and B_{12}
Aspirin	Depletes B_1, B_{12} and folic acid
Diuretics	Deplete B complex vitamins, especially B_6
Lipid lowering drugs	Absorption of folic acid and B_{12} decreased
Oestrogens and the Pill	Raise the requirements for B_2, B_6, B_{12} and folic acid
Penicillins Tetracyclines	Decrease the absorption of B_1, B_2, B_5, B_6, B_{12} and folic acid. Supplements should not be taken closer than two hours before or after a dose of these medicines. Supplemental B_2 decreases lincomycin and tetracycline's activity
Urinary tract anti-infectives	Decrease the absorption of B_1 and B_{12}

Also: smoking and stress increase the body's need for B complex vitamins, diabetes increases the need for choline, illness and injury increase the need for folic acid, and taking more than 750 mg of vitamin C a day can deplete B_{12}.

VITAMIN C

Vitamin C acts as a detoxifier in the body and protects against damage from smoke and chemical fumes.

Vitamin C protects cells from damage caused by a wide range of chemicals and pollutants, and it also aids in their excretion from the body. Like vitamin A, it provides protection from the damaging and cancer-causing substances in tobacco smoke.

Vitamin C is one of the most important vitamins for minimizing the effects of environmental pollution on the body. It plays a role in the detoxification and excretion of a wide range of toxic chemicals. In tandem with zinc it helps to reduce lead and cadmium toxicity and levels of a number of other toxic minerals. Exposure to certain indoor pollutants increases the need for this vitamin, and it is particularly important for smokers or those who are exposed to sidestream smoke. Vitamin C helps the liver to break down toxic materials and is a heavy-metal antagonist. Research suggests that it reduces the toxic effects of chlorinated pesticides and generally speeds up the detoxification of chemicals. Vitamin C also inhibits the production of nitrosamines which are formed from nitrates in the digestive tract.

Vitamin C works in water soluble regions of the cells. Manganese augments the antioxidant value of vitamin C, and its levels in the blood decrease when there is insufficient vitamin A.

How Much Should I Take?

Each cigarette smoked, or the equivalent exposure to someone else's, increases the need for vitamin C by 25 mg. You would have to eat 2 to 4 oranges to replace this.

An optimum intake of vitamin C with bioflavonoids for adults exposed to pollutants and high levels of stress could range from 500 mg to 1000 mg a day taken in doses of 250 mg with meals. Bioflavonoids protect vitamin C in the body and enhance its function. Vitamin C has not been shown to be toxic, although some people may experience slight burning during urination, loose bowel movements or skin rashes with doses over 500 mg. Humans and other primates lack the ability to synthesize this compound from glucose so it must be obtained from the diet. Body stores are depleted by stressors which include exposure to pollutants and chemicals.

> Supplements of vitamin C taken at the same time as B_6 interfere with its metabolism, and doses of vitamin C over 750 mg decrease B_{12}.

Ensure that B_{12}, B_6 and magnesium are supplied adequately in the diet if you intend to use optimum doses of vitamin C, but *always take B_6 and B_{12} at least two hours apart from the vitamin C.* If you suffer from gastric ulcers, take vitamin C as calcium ascorbate to avoid irritation, and if you are pregnant restrict your intake to no more than 750 mg a day.

It has been estimated that smokers may require as much as 30 percent more vitamin C every day than non-smokers. The French government recommends that smokers have 120 mg of vitamin C a day and non-smokers 80 mg. The British RDA of 30 mg a day is one of the lowest in the world. Some people experience intestinal wind when taking large doses of ascorbic acid. This is because when the acid contacts liquid in the intestines carbon dioxide is released. Vitamin C taken as mineral ascorbate is less likely to precipitate this condition.

Vitamin C's reaction with certain drugs

Medicine	Interaction with Vitamin C
Allopurinol gout medicines	May increase the rare side effect of kidney stones if taken during treatment with these drugs.
Anticoagulants	Over 500 mg of vitamin C taken twice a day with anticoagulants may decrease their effects.
Paracetamol	If paracetamol is being taken on a regular basis, avoid doses of vitamin C over 250 mg twice a day as it will decrease the excretion of the drug and increase the possibility of side effects.
Oral contraceptives	A daily dose of more than 750-1000 mg of vitamin C taken while using the Pill increases the availability of oestrogen in the body and raises the chance of experiencing oestrogen-related side effects.
Sulphonamide or Trimethoprim antibiotics	Doses of vitamin C over 250 mg taken during a course of these antibiotics may increase the rare chance of kidney damage.
Quinidine Antiarrhythmics	More than 200 mg of vitamin C taken with these drugs can decrease their therapeutic effects.

Warning

Vitamin C should only be taken with anxiolitics, tranquillizers, and corticosteroids *under medical supervision.* High doses of vitamin C can affect the accuracy of certain medical tests, including those to determine the presence of blood in the stool.

What Are the Best Dietary Sources?

Vitamin C, or ascorbic acid, is a water soluble vitamin which is not stored in the body in significant quantities, and for this reason, it is important that it is supplied regularly in the diet – especially when you are exposed to pollutants. Contrary to popular belief, oranges are not the ultimate source of vitamin C; in fact they are quite low on the list.

This nutrient is easily destroyed by light, air, heat and oxidation. When cooking foods which contain vitamin C there is a greater loss if using iron or copper pans, especially if baking soda or powder is added to the food.

Home-made rosehip syrup is a natural supplemental source of vitamin C.

To make rosehip syrup, pick rosehips from a source away from agricultural chemicals and roadside pollution; they will be ripe in late summer. Wash well and put in a non-aluminium pan with enough water to cover them. Put the lid on and bring to the boil, then simmer until about half of the water has evaporated. Strain and add raw, uncooked honey to taste. Store in the refrigerator.

Sources of vitamin C

Higher Sources	Lower Sources
Acerola cherries/juice	White cabbage
Rosehip syrup	Mustard and cress
Blackcurrants	Blackberries
Guavas (fresh)	Gooseberries
Guavas (canned)	Grapefruit
Parsley	Lychees
Kale	Other fruit and vegetables
Horseradish	

Higher Sources	Lower Sources
Broccoli tops Green peppers Tomato purée (fresh) Brussels sprouts Chives Lemons Cauliflower Watercress Strawberries Cabbage (savoy and red) Oranges/fresh juice Mustard tops	A small quantity of vitamin C is found in cod roe, meat, fish and cow's milk

The foods are listed in descending order of potency

What Decreases My Vitamin C Levels?

Petrol fumes Smoking Exposure to air pollution	Increase the body's requirements for vitamin C because it is used to protect cells and eliminate toxicants, heavy metals and pollutants.
Antacids Antibiotics	Decrease the absorption of vitamin C.
Antihistamines Aspirin Cortisone Diuretics	Regular use depletes vitamin C.

Also: vitamin C requirements are increased by high fever, regular strenuous physical activity, surgery, injury or dental treatment, high stress, and high alcohol intake.

VITAMIN E

Vitamin E protects cells against free radicals generated by chemical pollutants.

Vitamin E works with vitamin A and selenium to protect the liver and cells from the damaging effects of pollutants, including ozone and smog. This oil-soluble vitamin is one of the main antioxidant nutrients, and applies its antioxidant action on the cell walls. Tissues in direct contact with oxygen, particularly the lungs, are primary candidates for oxidative damage, and vitamin E can protect against this. It also protects red blood cells against free radical damage from ozone exposure. Like vitamin C, vitamin E counteracts toxicants inhaled from polluted air; it increases resistance to smog, infections, arthritis and cancer and enhances the activity and antioxidant effects of vitamins A, B, C, selenium and zinc. Vitamin E heightens the performance of B and T cells, lymphocytes which are an integral part of the immune system, and prevents saturated fats and vitamin A from breaking down and combining with other substances that may become harmful to the body.

In common with other antioxidants, vitamin E works by uniting with oxygen, preventing it from being converted to harmful peroxides. By inhibiting oxidative damage to cell membranes, the integrity of the cells is maintained and this can have a protective effect against the genesis of cancer. Vitamin E works in oil soluble regions of the cell with vitamin A.

How Much Should I Take?

Regular exposure to oxidizing pollutants in the air has increased everyone's basic need for vitamin E, especially those in cities and polluted areas, or those who smoke. Adults should aim for an intake of between 200 to 400 iu a day to benefit from vitamin E's preventative effects and antioxidant enhancing capacity.

Our requirements for vitamin E have been increasing as more and more pollutants and chemicals are introduced into the environment. Wholewheat, especially the wheatgerm, is one of the highest dietary sources of vitamin E, but the processing and refining of grains (into white flour, for instance) and the heat or solvent treatment of vegetable oils has diminished the average daily intake of this nutrient.

Vitamin E has not proven toxic, although in susceptible people, substantial doses taken over a period of time may cause fatigue, muscle weakness and possibly gastro intestinal upsets. An excessive intake of supplemental vitamin E can decrease thyroid function.

> Supplemental vitamin E may temporarily raise blood pressure in those with a history of clinical hypertension. In this instance, 50 to 100 iu is commonly a safe dose. Any further increments should be made gradually and with a doctor's advice.

Anyone taking prescribed medicines for a heart condition should consult a doctor before taking doses of vitamin E over 50 to 100 iu. For some people with mitral stenosis, taking vitamin E in doses over 100 iu every day may cause an increase in chest pains, and patients who have had rheumatic fever should not take vitamin E unless under medical supervision. *Insulin dependent diabetics who wish to take supplemental vitamin E should do so only after consulting their doctor,* as the dose of insulin may need to be adjusted in accordance with the amount of vitamin E to be taken. Diabetes increases the body's need for this nutrient.

> Inorganic iron and vitamin E antagonize each other's absorption and should be taken 10 hours apart. Iron supplements listed with ferrous as a prefix are organic; those with ferric as a prefix are inorganic.

What Are the Best Dietary Sources?

> Wheatgerm oil and wheatgerm are the best natural food 'supplements' of vitamin E, but care must be taken to ensure that they are fresh.

Vitamin E is destroyed by cooking in open pans, particularly by deep fat frying. Some may also be lost during commercial deep freezing. Cold pressed and virgin vegetable oils retain more vitamin E than solvent or heat processed and refined oils. The cloudier an oil, the less it has been refined.

Sources of vitamin E

Oil Sources	Food Sources
Wheatgerm oil	Egg yolk
Soyabean oil	Muesli
Cottonseed oil	Brown rice
Safflower oil	Turnip greens
Rice bran oil	Salmon
Sunflower oil	Peas/beans
Peanut oil	Liver
Cod liver oil	
Linseed oil	
Olive oil	

The foods are listed in descending order of potency; oils are the richest source

What Affects My Vitamin E Levels?

Pollutants including lead Smoking	Increase the body's requirements for vitamin E.
Liquid paraffin Laxatives	Decrease the body's absorption of fat soluble nutrients including vitamin E.
Lipid lowering drugs	These drugs alter the way the body metabolizes fats, and absorption of fat soluble vitamins including vitamin E is decreased.

Also: vitamin E requirements are increased with a high dietary intake of polyunsaturated oils or fats and rancid cooking oils, nuts and seeds, infection, smoking, and drinking chlorinated water. Extra vitamin E is also needed when stress levels are high and during pregnancy, lactation and menopause.

SELENIUM

Selenium aids in the body's elimination of lead, cadmium, mercury, pesticides, herbicides and drug residues.

Selenium has a role in establishing tolerance to pollutants in the environment; it also protects against damage from radiation. It aids in maintaining the stability of the cell membranes and is instrumental in ridding the body of cadmium, lead, arsenic and mercury. It protects against damage done by free radicals and other substances that inhibit immune response. Studies indicate that selenium has the potential to prevent carcinogens from being converted into actual cancer-causing agents in the body.

Selenium is one of the main antioxidants along with vitamins A, C, and E and is believed to cut down on free radical damage to DNA molecules. It protects the body from inflammatory toxic chemicals, the sun's rays, and damage done by the normal metabolic processes. It is a vital component of the free radical scavenging enzyme glutathione peroxidase. Therapeutic doses of this mineral administered to those with severe chemical sensitivity has resulted in an improvement. Selenium is also one of a number of nutrients involved in the body's elimination of drug residues and the maintenance of healthy liver function.

How Much Should I Take?

In common with zinc, men need more selenium than women as almost half of their body-content of the mineral is found in the testicles and seminal ducts; it is lost with seminal fluid.

Selenium is a trace mineral and is therefore required only in very small quantities. However, increased pollution, food processing, refining and exposure to heavy metals like lead have raised selenium requirements while its intake has been lowered. The growing scarcity of this mineral is coinciding with an increasing need for its powers as an immune system stimulant, antioxidant and heavy metal detoxifier. Consequently it is becoming more important to ensure that the diet contains sufficient sources of selenium.

Selenium used to be considered to be a poison, but it was later discovered to be an essential mineral for prevention of liver-tissue degeneration in rats. It is now considered to be an essential trace mineral for humans. Supplements from organically bound selenium yeast have a lower toxicity potential than sodium selenite, although this is the supplemental form recommended if there is an intolerance to yeast due to candida infection or allergy. Supplements of either form are considered safe at doses up to 200 mcg.

> Take supplements of zinc and selenium well apart. Ideally, take selenium in the morning and zinc at night, as they interfere with each other's absorption when taken in supplemental doses.

What Are the Best Dietary Sources?

Selenium levels in the soil differ throughout the world; Europe has low levels, with the exception of Norfolk in the UK. It is found mainly in areas which contain volcanic ash.

> Garlic contains the highest level of selenium of any plant. It protects the body against pollutants, heavy metals, poisons, and free radicals. Selenium stimulates the immune system.

Modern farming methods, loss of topsoil, and food processing have contributed to the scarcity of this mineral in foods. Selenium-rich, high-protein Canadian grain is no longer imported for use in the UK due to high EEC Levies, and the European grains now used come from very low selenium areas. Minerals are relatively stable when cooked or heated, but some selenium may be lost into water when cooking foods.

Sources of Selenium

Sources

Organ meats
Fish
Muscle meats
Whole grains and cereals
Dairy products
Brewer's yeast
Asparagus
Garlic
Other vegetables
Fruit

The foods are listed in descending order of potency, but where and how they are grown and the degree to which they have been processed determines their actual selenium content

What Increases My Selenium Requirements?

Exposure to:

Pollutants
Heavy metals
Toxic chemicals
Cigarette smoke
Free radical oxidation
Infection

Also: The body's requirement for selenium is increased during prolonged or heavy exposure to oxidizing pollutants, and when the immune system is taxed.

ZINC

The dangers of toxic metals are reduced when there is adequate zinc in the body.

The toxicity of lead and cadmium is reduced in the presence of zinc, and it also stimulates the removal of toxic metals from the body. Zinc is so important that a deficiency can allow the precipitation of toxic metal poisoning, particularly with exposure to lead or cadmium.

Zinc is important for people who are exposed to high levels of lead, such as that from vehicle exhaust, and for smokers. It acts as a cell membrane stabilizer and so protects them against free radical attack. It is also vital in the production of the body's antioxidant, superoxide dismutase. When teamed with vitamins A, C and E it can slow some of the damage caused by free radical attack. Zinc also assists in the transport of vitamin A from storage in the liver and other organs to the rest of the body.

How Much Should I Take?

An optimum intake of zinc for adults can range from 15 to 30 mg a day, especially with unavoidable exposure to air pollution, heavy metals and toxic chemicals.

Zinc is relatively non-toxic, and excess is excreted in the urine. A high intake (over 50 mg of zinc a day) may interfere with copper metabolism and increase the need for vitamin A-rich foods.

What Are the Best Dietary Sources?

Shellfish, especially oysters, are a good dietary source of zinc, although they are not necessarily the best. They can also be a significant source of pollutants, since they feed on the bottom of the ocean and absorb chemicals dumped into the sea.

The content and availability of zinc in foods is influenced by processing and refining and other less obvious factors. The addition of EDTA (ethylene-diamine-tetra-acetate) and polyphosphate complexing agents to foods reduces the amount of zinc available for absorption, while a vegetarian or vegan diet may be high in phytic acid which decreases the body's absorption of zinc. Phytic acid is found mainly in grains, unleavened bread such as matzo, nuts, legumes, and some tubers. Dietary fibre binds strongly with zinc and prevents its absorption.

Cooking foods (except in copper utensils) reduces the adverse effects of phytic acid and fibre on zinc absorption although zinc is water soluble so it may be lost into cooking water. Fermented foods such as miso contain the enzyme phytase which can offset phytic acid's effects. Sourdough and breads which have risen with yeast do not contain phytic acid, so the zinc in the grains is available to the body.

Main Food Sources

Oysters
Liver
Brewer's yeast
Shrimps
Crab
Beef
Cheese
Sardines
Wholemeal bread
Eggs
Rye bread
Chicken
Peas
Pumpkin seeds

The foods are listed in descending order of potency

What Decreases My Zinc Levels?

Digitalis Corticosteroids Thiazide diuretics	These drugs can decrease or deplete zinc levels, especially when taken in high doses or over a long period of time.
The Pill Oestrogens	Taking either the Pill or oestrogens raises the body's requirements for zinc. During Pill use, copper levels are raised, which decreases zinc absorption.

Also: zinc is depleted during excessive perspiration, during stress from surgery and burns, and when too much folic acid, calcium, copper, manganese and iron are ingested. A high carbohydrate/low protein intake and a high alcohol consumption also deplete zinc. Men need more zinc than women; it is found in high concentrations in the reproductive system and is lost in seminal fluid.

> Zinc is best taken at night or at least away from meals. Folic acid in vitamin B complex supplements, eggs, milk and phytates in cereal decreases zinc's bio-availability.

CALCIUM, IRON AND MAGNESIUM

Calcium, iron and magnesium are involved in the body's defence against chemical and heavy metal pollution.

Calcium is important for influencing immunity to cancer, and it can protect the body against radiation. In tandem with magnesium, calcium binds with radioactive materials and carries them out of the body. A diet low in calcium and vitamin D will encourage the body to take up more ingested lead. Sources of calcium include dairy products, especially cheese and yogurt which is easily digested, canned fish, nuts and pulses, sesame seeds, brewer's yeast, carob, seaweeds (especially hijiki), vegetables, nuts, eggs, oatmeal, fruit and wheatgerm.

Iron deficiency can weaken the immune function. Deficiencies may be partly due to lead and cadmium pollution which reduce the availability of iron in food. Drinking tea with a meal also greatly reduces iron absorption. Sources include brewer's yeast, liver, soya flour, parsley, dried peaches, apricots, figs and prunes, canned sardines, oatmeal and wholemeal bread. The herb and fruit tonic Floradix is a good natural iron supplement.

Magnesium is essential for helping the body to dispose of ammonia, a chemical found in some household cleaning products, cigarette smoke, and hair permanents. It can also help in the elimination of lead from the body. Good sources of magnesium include soy beans, cashews, almonds and brazil nuts, brewer's yeast, wholewheat flour, brown rice, seafoods, bananas, dried fruit, meat and vegetables.

AMINO ACIDS

Sulphur-containing amino acids bind with toxic substances and remove from the body heavy metal deposits including lead and mercury. They are also vital components of the body's free radical defence system and are noted protectors against the effects of radiation. People who are extremely sensitive to environmental chemicals may have low cysteine or low taurine levels.

Cysteine and cystine are sulphur-containing amino acids found in high concentration in eggs. They are instrumental in the removal of heavy metals including lead and mercury, and L-cysteine protects against radiation. These amino acids are antioxidant and work together with L-glutathione to inhibit cross-linking produced by free radicals.

L-cysteine teams with vitamins B_1, C and B_6 to protect the body against aldehydes found in smog, tobacco and wood smoke. It also reduces the risk of damage such as emphysema resulting from smoking.

Vitamin C and L-glutathione keep cysteine and cystine in soluble form for maximum utilization and absorption. *People with diabetic tendencies should not use large supplemental doses of cysteine except under supervision.* Cysteine is best taken in supplemental form with vitamin C. Foods containing cysteine include soy beans, eggs, brazils and cashews, sesame and sunflower seeds and brewer's yeast.

Methionine is a sulphur-containing amino acid which acts as a powerful detoxification agent capable of the removal of toxic levels of heavy metals from the body. Methionine is an antioxidant and as such is a free radical scavenger. It is involved in the production of glutathione peroxidase, a powerful antioxidant enzyme. Foods rich in methionine include beef, chicken, fish, soy beans, eggs, cottage cheese, liver, sardines, yogurt, pumpkin seeds, sesame seeds, lentils, beans, onions and garlic.

Glutathione acts against free radicals by combining with their derivatives in the liver, lungs and other organs, neutralizing their reactivity. It is excreted in the urine and bile along with the neutralized or stabilized radical fragments. It also detoxifies lead, cadmium, mercury and aluminium by carrying them harmlessly from the body.

EPA
(Eicosapentanoic acid)

Fish oil supplements containing EPA are being studied in connection with their possible ability to reduce the spread of tumour cells and transform them into benign cells. In the laboratory, cancer cells grown on a medium containing EPA were found to have a decreased ability to spread. The research is still in progress and is by no means conclusive, but EPA's addition to the diet may prove to be useful in deterring the spread of cancer cells.

GARLIC

Garlic is a potent detoxifier which contains many nutrients, including the trace minerals selenium and germanium. It protects the liver against toxicants like carbon tetrachloride and may be effective in treating lead, mercury and other heavy metal poisonings. Its sulphur molecules are highly active and can bind with heavy metals, slow the clotting activity of blood platelets, and inhibit the harmful action of oxygen (free radical damage), possibly limiting damage to the body's cell membranes.

CHLORELLA

Chlorella is a form of algae which has very promising detoxification capabilities. It has been used to detoxify people suffering from PCB (polychlorobiphenyl) exposure and to detoxify chemicals breathed in when painting. Chlorella is particularly important in assisting the removal of hydrocarbons and toxicants such as cadmium, mercury, lead, pesticides, uranium and aluminium. Clinical studies carried out in Japan at the Kitakyushu

City University Institute for Environmental Pollution Research reported its detoxifying benefits to humans.

For detoxification with chlorella, tablets or granules should be taken on an empty stomach. In some cases there may be an initial increase in intestinal wind, but this will cease as the system is restored to normal activity. In general it takes from 3 to 4 weeks for general detoxification using chlorella; however, problems like bad breath, body odour and constipation often respond within 7 to 10 days.

8

A–Z of Useful Addresses and Suppliers

It is unnecessary to live in a chemically induced sterile environment, nor do we have to suffer the ill effects of paint vapours or adhesives after a weekend of DIY mania. The number of alternative environmentally 'friendly' products now extends from washing powder to paints, varnishes and bed frames.

There are simple, healthier alternatives to the chemicals we have come to consider as essential for household cleanliness. Our grandparents can probably remember when shops sold soap flakes for cleaning clothes and floors, sticky paper for catching flies and beeswax for polishing furniture. Now there is an overwhelming variety of products which promise to make life easier, surroundings more pleasant smelling, and send germs running away screaming. Although many of these products do reduce the effort required to keep a home clean, they often do so at the expense of the environment and our health.

This chapter is intended as a guide to some of the 'green' products available. However, although we personally use many of the products listed, we cannot endorse them. The chapter also includes associations and other contacts – if you think there are omissions please write to us care of Fontana Paperbacks as this feedback will help us when compiling future editions.

A–Z Index

ADDRESSES, MISCELLANEOUS

ACTION GROUPS

National Anti-Fluoridation Campaign
36 Station Road
Thames Ditton
Surrey, KT7 0NS
Telephone (081) 398 2117

Contact them for more details and membership information, enclosing an SAE with any enquiries.

National Campaign Against Solvent Abuse
Enterprise Centre
444 Brixton Road
London, SW9 8EJ
Telephone (071) 733 7330

For more information please send an SAE with your enquiry.

National Society for Clean Air
136 North Road
Brighton
Sussex, BN1 1RG

The National Society for Clean Air and Environmental Protection is a non-governmental, non-political organization and charity. Founded in 1899, the society's objectives include promoting clean air through the reduction of air pollution and other contaminants while having due respect for other aspects of the environment. NSCA brings together pollution expertise from industry, local and central government, technical, academic and institutional bodies. The society has vast resources of data on all types of air pollution. They produce a journal called *Clean Air* and numerous information leaflets, and their Information Officer will answer general questions about air quality. Please enclose an SAE with any enquiries.

BUILDING AND DESIGN SERVICES

Architectural Salvage Index
Hutton and Rostron
Netley House
Gomshall
Guildford
Surrey
Telephone (048 641) 3221

This company supplies recycled building materials.

Association of Environment Conscious Builders
Windlake House
The Pump Field
Codley
Glos, GL11 5DX

Send an SAE for more details.

Building Use Services Ltd
David Tong
53–54 Newman Street
London, W1P 3PG
Telephone (071) 580 8848

Specialists in designing and creating healthy indoor environments.

Busch Masheder Associates
Telephone (0799) 26575

Designers of 'The Green Home'. Busch Masheder are an architectural group who specialize in building biology. They also supply AURO organic DIY products (see p.266).

Constructive Individuals
53 Adys Road
London, SE15 4DX
Telephone (071) 639 0140

If you want to build your own home, contact Constructive Individuals for more information.

Ecological Design Association
c/o Gaia
66 Charlotte Street
London, W1P 1LR
Telephone (071) 323 4010 Ext 204

The aims of this association are to promote the design of ecological and people-friendly environments and communities, education, setting of standards for ecological projects, services, materials and products, and to encourage interdisciplinary contacts between people involved with building design, orthodox and complementary medicine, manufacturers, retailers and the media. Many more projects are planned for the future. For more information contact EDA and include an SAE with your enquiry.

DOWSING

The British Society of Dowsers
Sycamore Cottage
Tamley Lane
Hastingleigh
Ashford
Kent, TN25 5HW
Telephone (0233) 75 253

Dowsing is most commonly associated with finding water, but it is also used for several other purposes including geophysical and site surveying, agricultural and soil testing. The society issues a quarterly journal to its members and gives public lectures. They also hold specialized courses and have a library. Dowsing equipment and books are sold at meetings and by mail order. Please send an SAE to the society when you write for more information and membership details.

ENERGY SOURCES, ALTERNATIVE

British Wind Energy Association
4 Hamilton Place
London, W1V 0BQ

BWEA is a professional association comprising engineers, scientists, academics and anyone interested in working in the field of wind energy. BWEA produce a quarterly newsletter, 'Windirections', and a technical journal on wind energy six times a year. For more information about the association, its work, products and equipment, newsletter and membership details, please send an SAE with your enquiry.

Centre for Alternative Technology
Llwyngwern Quarry
Machynlleth
Powys
Wales, SY20 9AZ
Telephone (0654) 2400

This organization is a registered charity and all profits go towards funding the Centre For Alternative Technology. They carry a wide range of 'green' books, energy efficient and renewable energy equipment such as solar and wind powered items, rechargeable and less toxic batteries, energy efficient lights, household and personal items, recycled paper products including stationery, unbleached coffee filters, continuous computer listing paper, children's hobby items, organic gardening products, etc. The centre also has a knowledgeable staff who can deal with enquiries on a wide range of alternative technology subjects, and they also run 2–4 day residential courses – send an SAE for full details and costs.

The Solar Energy Society UK
Kings College
Camden Hill Road
Kensington
London, W8 7AH
Telephone (071) 333 4314

This society promotes solar energy in all its aspects including organizing national and international conferences. They also publish technical books on solar energy and provide information through newsletters and other documentation to members and the general public. For more information and details of membership write with an SAE.

ENVIRONMENT GROUPS

CLEAR
3 Endsleigh Street
London, WC1H 0DD
Telephone (071) 278 9686

CLEAR campaigns for lead-free air. Send a large SAE with any enquiries.

The Commonwork Centre
Bore Place
Chiddingstone
Edenbridge
Kent, TN8 7AR
Telephone (0732) 463255

This centre is owned by the Commonwork Land Trust, an educational trust set up by Neil and Jenifer Wates in 1976. The purpose is to encourage the creative development of natural resources, including the talents and potential of people. A group of historic farm buildings has been converted to form the centre which offers workshops, accommodation and space for groups to hold workshops or courses/seminars, join organized projects or develop their own in areas of ecology, arts, holistic health, Development Education, and an educational programme for schools. There is a 300-cow dairy enterprise, a facility for producing hand-made bricks, an ecology project, special projects for the disabled and those under stress, an organic garden, a pottery and kiln, a field trail and a nearby nature reserve. There is provision for wheelchair access. Contact the centre for booking forms and more details. (See also Super Natural Ltd on p.258.)

Friends of the Earth
Main office: *Membership enquiries:*
26–28 Underwood Street   Membership Department
London, N1 7JQ   Freepost
Telephone (071) 490 1555   Mitcham
                                            Surrey, CR4 9AR

Campaigns on issues which affect the environment. They carry an extensive range of literature and there are local groups throughout the country. They produce information on air quality and carry a publications list. To obtain their catalogue see the details under Mail Order (p.263) in this chapter.

Gaia Foundation
18 Well Walk
London, NW3

Publish information on Gaia concepts. The Gaia hypothesis states that left to themselves, natural systems maintain their own balance. That there is integrity through feed-back loops, whereby both environment and organism have a cause and effect relationship with each other. For more information write to them and include an SAE.

Greenpeace
30–31 Islington Green
London, N1 8BR
Telephone (071) 354 5100

Campaign throughout the world on issues which include the protection of the environment and wildlife. Send an SAE for details of membership and further information.

Institute of Environmental Health Officers
Chadwick House
Rushworth Street
London, SE1 0QT
Telephone (071) 928 6006

This organization can arrange soil analysis to detect contamination by lead or other substances.

International Institute of Biological Husbandry
9 Station Approach
Needham Market
Ipswich
Suffolk

This organization has links with many organic groups.

Soil Association
86 Colston Street,
Bristol, BS1 5BB
Telephone (0272) 290661

The Soil Association promotes organic farming and works towards decreasing pesticide usage. Write with an SAE for membership details and more information.

World Wide Fund for Nature UK
Panda House
Weyside Park
Godalming
Surrey, GU7 1XR
Telephone (0483) 426 444

The WWF works towards conserving nature and natural resources. Write to them with an SAE for details of membership and more information.

FINANCIAL SERVICES, GREEN

The Ecology Building Society
18 Station Road
Cross Hills
Nr Keighley
West Yorkshire, BD20 7EH
Telephone (0535) 35933

The society was founded in 1981 to provide a means of finance for purchasing ecologically sound properties and has grown into a specialist Building Society. Organic smallholdings and farms, derelict but sound buildings which would otherwise have been abandoned, and homes for people running small ecological businesses are some of the areas where the society lends money.

Greencard
Bank of Credit and Commerce International
BCC Card Centre
Radnor House
Harlands Road
Haywards Heath
Sussex, RH16 1LU

Every time you use the Greencard, a donation is made to green organizations and charities of your choice. Interest rates are lower than the major credit cards.

Barchester Investment (0722 331241) and **Bromige & Partners** (071 491 0558) are worth contacting for further information on 'green' investment.

HEALTH GROUPS

Action Against Allergy
43 The Downs
London, SW20 8H6
Telephone (081) 947 5082

Help for allergy sufferers. For more information send a large SAE.

Action on Smoking and Health (ASH)
5–11 Mortimer Street
London, W1N 7RH
Telephone (071) 637 9843

A charitable organization which gathers information on the dangers of smoking and offers advice on how to stop. It was set up by the Royal College of Physicians in London. For more details about ASH or a free 'Give-up Pack', send a 1st class stamped, self-addressed envelope with your enquiry or request.

Asthma Society
300 Upper Street
Islington
London, N1 2XX
Telephone (071) 266 2260

This society raises funds for asthma research and has more than 160 branches in the UK. For more information send a large SAE.

Breakspear Hospital for Allergy and Environmental Medicine
High Street
Abbots Langley
Hertfordshire, WD5 0PU
Telephone (0923) 261333

The Breakspear Hospital is one of the few facilities of its kind in the world and is Europe's first major purpose-built environmental medicine hospital. For more information write with an SAE to the hospital. Dr Jean Monro is the Medical Director.

British Medical Association
Telephone (071) 387 4499

Contact the BMA for information about pesticides and human illness.

British Society for Allergy and Environmental Medicine
The Secretary
Acorns
Romsey Road
Cadnam
Southampton, SO4 2NN

For more information about the society and its work send an SAE with your enquiry.

Dulwich Health Society
130 Gypsy Hill
London, SE19 1PL

Can detect and advise on geopathic stress. (See also the British Society of Dowsers on p.236.)

Environmental Medicine Foundation
Symondsbury House
Bridport
Dorset, DT6 6HB
Telephone (0308) 22956

This foundation carries out research into the treatment of illness caused by environmental factors. Send an SAE with any enquiries.

Foresight
Association for Preconceptual Care
The Old Vicarage
Church Lane
Witley
Godalming
Surrey, GU8 5PN

Foresight can give information on fertility related to nutrition, parental health, allergy and environment. They have a range of publications and free leaflets and can also provide the name of a local doctor in private practice who runs a foresight clinic. Please send an SAE with any enquiries.

Integration
Brighton's NLP Development Centre
4a Kemp Town Place
Kemp Town
Sussex
Telephone (0273) 680523

In London:
New Cross Natural Therapy Centre
Telephone (081) 469 0858
Contact: Karin Stratford

Integration is an organization which devotes time to running personal growth workshops and giving personal counselling on numerous issues including health and stopping addictive behaviour such as alcohol and drug abuse and smoking. The therapy used is fast, effective, holistic and enjoyable. For more information, please send an SAE with your enquiry.

National Eczema Society
Tavistock House East
Tavistock Square
London, WC1H 9SR
Telephone (071) 388 4097

Information and advice for sufferers and their families. For more information please send an SAE.

SAD Association
Mrs Jennifer Eastwood
51 Bracewell Road
London, W10 6AF
Telephone (081) 969 7028

A self-help organization for Seasonal Affective Disorder (SAD)
sufferers and their relatives. SADA sends information to enquirers,
produces a regular newsletter, makes local contacts and forms dis-
cussion groups throughout the country – it also offers support and
advice to people who need it. For membership details, telephone or
write with an SAE to the association. Members receive a quarterly
newsletter and the latest medical and consumer information plus
a list of contacts.

Women's Environmental Network
287 City Road
London, EC1V 1LA
Telephone (071) 490 2511

Established in 1988, this organization gives women information
about environmental problems that affect them specifically. They
publish *Green Living Magazine* and campaign on a number of
issues. Write with an SAE for details of membership.

US ORGANIZATIONS

BIOELECTRICITY

International Society for Bioelectricity
PO Box 82
Boston
Massachusetts, 02135
USA

CLINICAL ECOLOGY

The American Academy of Environmental Medicine (AAEM)
Box 16106
Denver
Colorado, 80216
USA

Environmental Health Care Centre
8345 Walnut Hill Lane
Suite 205
Dallas
Texas, 75231
USA

HEAL (Human Ecology Action League)
PO Box 1369
Evanston
Illinois, 60204
USA

Society for Clinical Ecology
2005 Franklin Street
Suite 490
Denver
Colorado, 80205
USA

HOLISTIC MEDICINE

American Holistic Medical Association
6932 Little River Turnpike
Annadale
Virginia, 22003
USA

NATUROPATHY

National Association of Naturopathic Physicians
John Bastyr College
2613 N. Stevens
~oma
~n. 98407

ORTHOMOLECULAR PSYCHIATRY

Academy of Orthomolecular Psychiatry
PO Box 372
Manhasset
NY 11030
USA

PESTICIDES INFORMATION SERVICES

National Pesticide Telecommunications Network
0101 (800) 858 7378

Texas Technical University
Health Sciences Centre
School of Medicine
Department of Preventive Medicine and Community Health
Lubbock
Texas, 79430
USA

WASTE DISPOSAL

Asbestos Information Centre
St Andrew's House
22-28 High Street
Epsom
Surrey, KT19 8AH
Telephone (03727) 42055

For information on all aspects of asbestos, contact this centre enclosing an SAE.

Asbestos Removal Contractors Association
1 High Street
Chelmsford
Essex, CM1 1BE
Telephone (0245) 259744

British Waste Paper Association
21 Devonshire Street
London, W1

HM Inspectorate of Pollution
Department of the Environment
Romney House
43 Marsham Street
London, SW1P 3PY
Telephone (071) 212 8981

Contact the DoE for information about hazardous waste and environmental issues.

Institute of Environmental Health Officers
Chadwick House
Rushworth Street
London, SE1 0QT
Telephone (071) 928 6006

London Hazard Centre
3rd floor, Headlands House
308 Grays Inn Road
London, WC1X 8DS
Telephone (071) 837 5605

Advice and publications on hazards at work and in the community. For more information send a large SAE.

London Waste Regulatory Authority
Hazardous Waste Unit
Room N4B
County Hall
London, SE1 7PB

LWRA will collect a small quantity of asbestos and household chemicals. Outside London contact your local Town Hall: Department of the Environment.

HOUSEHOLD AND GARDENING PRODUCTS

BEDS AND BEDDING

Alphabeds
8 Foscote Mews
London, W9 2HH
Telephone (071) 289 2464 or (0559) 935 428

Alphabeds sell natural bedding, self-assembly wooden beds, and metal-free orthopaedic mattresses. Bed frames are finished with non-toxic oils and waxes and mattresses are filled with natural materials covered with unbleached cotton. Contact them for a catalogue.

Dunlopillo UK
Customer Services Department:
Telephone (0423) 872411

Dunlopillo make natural latex mattresses with no metal springs. Latex contains millions of tiny air holes which act as a natural ventilation system for the body. There is no dust or fluff with this type of mattress. Dunlopillo mattresses should be available from major department stores and independent outlets. Contact the customer services department if you need information about local stockists.

The Futon Company
654a Fulham Road
London, SW6 5RU
Telephone (071) 736 9190

The Futon Factory Ltd
192 Balls Pond Road
London, N1
Telephone (071) 226 4477

The Whole Thing Catalogue
School Lane
Dunham, Massey
Altrincham
Cheshire, WA14 5SZ
Telephone (061) 236 5116

Cotton bedding, amongst many other things – see under Mail
Order (p.263).

BODY CARE

Ainsworths Homoeopathic Pharmacy
Cavendish Street
London, W1

Ainsworths dispense homoeopathic remedies and will mail order
products throughout the country. Contact them for information
about their range of products.

Green Farm Nutrition Centre
Carry an extensive range of natural body care products including
supplements. See under Mail Order (p.263) for more information.

Healthy Bodycare
Manchester Road
Tunstead Milton
Whaley Bridge
Stockport
Cheshire, SK12 7ER
Telephone (0663) 732081

Healthy Bodycare manufacture and market a range of toiletry,
cosmetics and household detergent products. Goldreif is a
unique environmentally friendly multi-purpose cleaner which
works everywhere around the home and is great to pack for
holidays as it even washes clothes and dishes. Goldreif works in
salt water making it an indispensable cleaner for boating enthu-

siasts. Other products in the Healthy Bodycare range include baby products and dishwasher detergent. The company has a retail shop in Liverpool where special products are made to order. Contact Healthy Bodycare for details of stockists and products.

Vamose Products
PO Box 1446
London, W6 7AG
Telephone (071) 384 2817

This company produces a natural insect repellant for adults and a special one for children. Please contact them for further information on their products.

Weleda UK Ltd
Heanor Road
Ilkeston
Derbyshire, DE7 8DR
Telephone (0602) 309319

Weleda, founded in 1923, produce a full line of natural cosmetics manufactured from pure plant products, many of which are organically grown in their own gardens. The company has extremely high standards and does not compromise the quality or effectiveness of the products for marketing appeal. Weleda homoeopathic remedies include tablets and ointments. For natural tooth care the products range from toothpaste to mouthwash and the natural citrus or sage ozone-friendly deodorant works with a pump action. Weleda products are not tested on animals and the labels list all the ingredients. Weleda have a full mail order service and will supply details of stockists. For more information pick up Weleda's catalogue in health stores or send a large SAE to the above address for more information.

Wella International
Telephone (071) 387 9911

Wella has developed a 'green' perm called Novena which is based on natural plant extracts and is biodegradable. For more information contact Wella.

BOOKS

Books for a Change
52 Charing Cross Road
London, WC2
Telephone (071) 836 2315

This bookshop is devoted entirely to books on green issues.
They will mail order books and related merchandise.

CLEANING AND HOUSEKEEPING

Ark
498–500 Harrow Road
London, W9 3QA
Telephone (081) 968 6780

Ark is working to protect life and the natural environment. For
membership details write with an SAE. A range of Ark natural
household products is available in most supermarkets.

Bio-Saks
Biodegradable refuse sacks. For details of stockists, contact MMD
Advertising, Telephone (0635) 524526

Ecover
Full Moon
Steyning
Sussex, BN4 3DG
Telephone (0903) 879077

Ecover produce a full range of products which biodegrade in
up to five days and contain no harmful ingredients. They are
not tested on animals, and contain no phosphates, enzymes,
alkalis, optical whiteners, soda ash, or chemical bleaches. They
are available from wholefood stores and many supermarkets. The
range includes washing-up liquid, non-chlorine bleach, washing
powder, dishwasher liquid and rinse aid, wool wash, non-scratch

cream cleaner, fabric conditioner, floor cleaner, toilet cleaner, heavy-duty hand cleaner.

Ecover also publish an information handbook entitled *An Introduction to the Environmental Problems of Cleaning Products*.

Faith Products
22 Great King Street
Edinburgh, EH3 6QH
Telephone (031) 661 0900

Faith Products market their natural household products under the Clearspring label. They contain no harmful ingredients, are biodegradable, and are available from many wholefood stores. The range includes washing-up liquid (vegan), laundry liquid, and dishwasher liquid. The products are not tested on animals and are free of alkalis, phosphates, bleaches, optical whiteners, soda ash, and enzymes.

Healthy Bodycare
Manchester Road
Tunstead Milton
Whaley Bridge
Stockport
Cheshire, SK12 7ER
Telephone (0663) 732081

Healthy Bodycare manufacture and market a range of toiletry, cosmetics and household detergent products. Goldreif is a unique environmentally friendly multi-purpose cleaner manufactured by this company. It works everywhere around the home and is great to pack for holidays as it even washes clothes and dishes. Goldreif works in salt water making it an indispensable cleaner for boating enthusiasts. Other products in the Healthy Bodycare range include baby products and dishwasher detergent. The company has a retail shop in Liverpool where special products are made to order. Contact Healthy Bodycare for details of stockists and products.

Larkhall Natural Health plc
225 Putney Bridge Road
Putney
London, SW15 2PY
Telephone (081) 874 1130

Air Therapy is a unique, chemical-free, concentrated air freshener derived from a blend of pure organic essential oils distilled from fruits and herbs. Contact Larkhall for more information and details of suppliers in your area. Larkhall will also mail order Air Therapy.

North Cotswold Apiary & Vineyard
Telephone (0386) 841244

Suppliers of beeswax furniture polish.

FURNITURE AND CARPETS

Flokati Rug Company
Unit C
11b Weir Road
London, SW12
Telephone (081) 675 2442

Greek flokati rugs – hand-made, using wool washed with natural soaps to retain the oils that keep it supple.

Gaskell Carpets Ltd
Blackburn
Lancs
Telephone (0254) 085566

Make Berber 100% wool carpet. Available from most retailers or telephone for local stockists.

Vailima
Broomhall
Nantwich
Cheshire
Telephone (0270) 780626 (evenings)

Suppliers of ecological furniture.

GARDENING PRODUCTS

Atlas Organic Seeds
40 Victoria Street
Braintree
Essex

Contact them for a catalogue.

Blackwall Products
Unit 4
150 River Way
London, SE10 0BE

This company produces a recycled barrel composter. Contact them for more details about their products.

Chase Organics GB Ltd
Coombelands House
Addlestone
Surrey, KT15 1HY

Organic seeds. Contact them for a catalogue.

Cowpact Products
PO Box 595
Buckinghamshire, MK18 2RE
Telephone (029671) 3838

Suppliers of non-chemical organic products and a variety of garden composts and manures from Soil-Association-registered organic farms.

Cumulus Organics and Conservation Ltd
Timber Yard, Two Miles Lane
Highnam
Gloucestershire, GL2 8DW
Telephone (0452) 305814

This company supplies an organic starting kit, composts, fertilizers and an organic caterpillar killer.

Henry Doubleday Research Association (HDRA)
National Centre for Organic Gardening
Ryton on Dunsmore
Coventry, CV8 3LG
Telephone (0203) 303517

Keep up with organic gardening ideas and techniques. HDRA produce an organic gardening catalogue which runs the gamut from rare vegetable and fruit varieties to garden tools and natural pest controls. They run numerous research projects into safe gardening and growing and provide a free advice service to their members along with a quarterly newsletter. They work hard to promote chemical-free methods of husbandry and encourage organic home gardening. HDRA also sell organic houseplant food, composts and organic wines.

Koppert UK Ltd
PO Box 43
Tunbridge Wells
Kent, TN2 5BY

Suppliers of natural predator insect control. Contact them for more details.

The Nature Conservancy Council
Northminster House
Peterborough, PE1 1UA

The statutory body concerned with wildlife protection. They offer advice on timber treatments that are not harmful to bats.

The Pesticide Trust
c/o Earth Resources Research
258 Pentonville Road
London, N1 9JY

For more information about the work of this trust please write
with an SAE.

Pesticides Action Network (PAN) Europe
22 Rue des Bollandistes
1040 Brussels
Belgium

For more information, write to PAN enclosing an SAE.

The Royal Society for the Protection of Birds (RSPB)
The Lodge
Sands
Bedfordshire, SG19 2DL
Telephone (0767) 80551

Contact the RSPB for details of membership, booklets and leaflets.
Send an SAE with enquiries.

Rushall Organic Farms
Rushall Mill
The Manor
Upavon
Pewsey
Wilts

Rushall are licensed by the Soil Association and produce a variety
of organically grown grains. These are sold in bags from 2 lb up to
10 tonnes. The flour is stone ground at their mill, and they also
sell breads and organic dog biscuits. For more information and a
price list send an SAE with your enquiry. Rushall also have 'open
days' at the farm and their founder, Barry Wookey has written the
book, *Rushall, the Story of an Organic Farm* (see under Further
Reading).

Silvaperl Products Ltd
PO Box 8
Harrogate
North Yorkshire, HG2 8JW

Seaweed soil conditioner. Contact them for more information.

Stimgro Ltd
Unit 2B
Longfield Road
Tunbridge Wells
Kent, TN2 3EY
Telephone (0893) 36731

Stimgro sell natural organic products including an organic grow-bag, mosskiller and lawn tonic. Send an SAE for local stockists.

Suffolk Herbs
Sawyers Farm
Little Cornyards
Sudbury
Suffolk, CO10 0NY

Wild flowers, herbs, tools and books. Ask them for their catalogue.

Super Natural Ltd
Bore Place Farm
Chiddingstone
Edenbridge
Kent, TN8 7AR
Telephone (0732) 463255

This company produces natural gardening products to the organic standards of the Soil Association. They include garden compost, houseplant compost and liquid plant food. They are becoming available more widely, including in major supermarkets like Sainsburys. Contact them for more information and stockists. (See also Commonwork on p.238.)

Turning Worms and Organic Supplies
Perthi Yard
Llanrhystud
Aberystwyth
Dyfed, SY23 5EH
Telephone (09746) 240

This company sells an 'ecology box' for worm and organic composts. Contact them for more details.

Vamose Products
P.O. Box 1446
London, W6 7AG
Telephone (071) 384 2817

This company produces a natural insect repellant. Please contact them for further information on their products.

IONIZERS AND ELECTRICAL APPLIANCES

Amcor
Amcor House
19 Woodfield Road
London, W9 2BA
Telephone (071) 289 4433

Amcor has a wide range of ionizers including three domestic models, two versions of the Freshen Aire, and the Air Processor which filters and ionizes the air. Amcor also manufactures commercial and home air processors, electrostatic air cleaners, and dehumidifiers. The Dust Trap is also available for use with the Freshen Aire and will catch dust, soot and other pollutants that are drawn from the air, preventing them from settling on walls and furniture. The Freshen Aire models and the Air Processor produce negative ions with carbon fibres rather than needles. The units include a high and low on/off switch. Amcor will answer telephone or written enquiries.

Batteries:
Varta non cadmium batteries are available from most stockists.

ClearAir UK
PO Box 83
Covent Garden
London, WC2H 9AJ
Telephone (071) 379 7369

ClearAir produce the VM ionizer, which conforms to British
Safety Standard BS 3456. ClearAir donate 20p from each sale
to research into the prevention of asthma in children. They will
supply a comprehensive consumer package on request.

Ebac Ltd
Domestic and Commercial Sales Division
St Helen Trading Estate
Bishop Auckland
County Durham, DL14 9AL
Telephone (0388) 600023

Ebac manufacture environmental control equipment and specialize in dehumidifiers, air cleaners and air conditioning. They carry
a range of six domestic dehumidifiers, including a loft installed
unit. The Electronaire is a room air cleaner which traps minute
pollutant particles in an electronically polarized filter pad. It can
remove pollens, dust, ash, tobacco smoke and other allergens from
indoor air. For more information or for a stockist in your area
contact Ebac.

Healthplan
7 Bruno Place
Salmon Street
London, NW9 8PP

This company produces an electrical appliance called Filtair which
removes fumes, chemicals, smoke etc. from indoor air via a series
of filters using centrifugal force. For more information write to the
address above or telephone Mr Leonard Rose on (081) 205 6243.

LEDA (Leek Electrical Domestic Appliances)
Dairy House
Ford, Onecote
Nr Leek
Staffs, ST13 7RW
Telephone (05388) 300

LEDA produce the Sundomus and the Ion Drive ionizers. Both conform to British Safety Standard BS 3456. They are in the lower price range although the quality is high. The Ion Drive uses a rotor to discharge the negative ions, which has the advantage of avoiding loss of ions due to absorption by plastic casing. LEDA will answer written or telephone enquiries.

Mountain Breeze
Peel House
Peel Road
Skelmersdale
Lancs
Telephone (0695) 21155 (for local stockists)

Mountain Breeze produce a large range of room ionizers, a car ionizer, commercial and domestic air processing systems, and ion probes which are for use in home, animal and bird enclosures, greenhouses, and workshops. Their ionizers conform to British Safety Standard BS 3456. Mountain Breeze will answer telephone and written enquiries.

Oasis Ltd
PO Box 74
Poole
Dorset, BH15 2DZ
Telephone (0202) 672423

Oasis carry a wide range of ionizers, including models for the home, car, and a commercial range. The ionizers conform to British Safety Standard BS 3456. The Oasis room model has a fuse at the back of the appliance and includes an on/off button on the unit. Oasis will send information on request.

Vorwerk UK Ltd
Vorwerk House
Toutley Road
Wokingham
Berks, RG11 5QN
Telephone (0734) 794878
Commercial manager: James McAuley

The vacuum cleaner for asthma sufferers and those who are highly sensitive to house dust etc. Extremely efficient deep dust removal, and the bag contains a special filter through which dust particles and dust mites cannot escape. It also picks up grit which damages carpet fibres. This vacuum outperforms others on the market and has a particularly long life-expectancy. It is more expensive than most vacuum cleaners but is worth the investment. Contact Vorwerk for a demonstration or for more information.

LIGHTING

Full Spectrum Lighting (FSL)
Unit 4
Wye Trading Estate
London Road
High Wycombe
Bucks, HP11 1LH
Telephone (0494) 448727

FSL supplies full-spectrum light tubes which can be used in standard fluorescent tube fittings. They are available in sizes ranging from 18 inches to 8 feet (45–240 cm). FSL welcomes enquiries, by phone or letter, and will also provide advice and information on SAD (Seasonal Affective Disorder). They manufacture the special light boxes used in the medical research on SAD.

Wotan Lights Ltd
Wotan House
1 Gresham Way
Durnsford Road
London, SW19 8HU
Telephone (081) 947 1261

Wotan produce low-energy light bulbs for domestic and industrial use. Domestic bulbs are available from electrical shops. Contact Wotan for more information on the products or details of a stockist in your area. See also the Centre for Alternative Technology under Mail Order (p.264).

MAIL ORDER SERVICES

The following companies produce mail order catalogues of environmentally friendly products.

The Allergy Shop
2 Mount Place
Lewes
East Sussex, BN7 1YH

For a catalogue of non-allergenic products ranging from cleaners to cosmetics, send a 1st class stamp to the above address. There is also an allergy Helpline on 0273 472127.

Asdir Ltd
PO Box 306
Sharnbrook
Beds, MK44 1TQ

Contact Asdir for their catalogue of natural fibre clothing.

The Centre For Alternative Technology
Llwyngwern Quarry
Machynlleth
Powys
Wales, SY20 9AZ
Telephone (0654) 2400

(See page 237).

Cosmetics to Go Catalogue
29 High Street
Poole
Dorset, BH15 1AB
Telephone (0202) 686666

An innovative catalogue crammed full of really different natural cosmetic items from soap to sunblock; liquid stockings to cold cream; make-up to fruit facepacks. The company is also very environment conscious, is planting trees in their local area and uses biodegradable packaging.

Friends of the Earth Catalogue
26–28 Underwood Street
London, N1 7JQ
Telephone (071) 490 1555

A catalogue of diverse products produced without harming the environment or upsetting the ecological balance.

Green Farm Nutrition Centre
Burwash Common
Burwash
East Sussex, TN19 7LX
Telephone (0435) 882482

Green Farm sell natural products including vitamins and minerals, body care items, cosmetics and a vegetable fibre skin brush. They also carry natural bedding and specialized electrical products. Contact them for a catalogue.

Henry Doubleday Research Association
Jackie Gear
National Centre for Organic Gardening
Ryton on Dunsmore
Coventry, CV8 3LG
Telephone (0203) 303517

HDRA produce the *Organic Gardening Catalogue* filled with ideas and natural husbandry products.

Practical Alternatives Catalogue
Victoria House
Bridge Street
Rhayader
Powys, LD6 5AG
Telephone (0597) 810929

Extensive mail order catalogue of energy saving equipment with literature. Can also provide information on many products and alternative household options. The Director, Dr Stephens, BSc, MSc, FIOA, is a consultant in the Building Sciences and has set up the Solar Village, a community of 'Survivor Houses' in Wales. Send an SAE for more information, a price list of literature and a catalogue. A magazine called *Practical Alternatives* is also produced.

Traidcraft Catalogue
Kingsway
Gateshead
Tyne and Wear, NE11 0NE
Telephone (091) 491 0591

Over 650 products including Third World crafts, jewellery and accessories, recycled paper products, foods, household items and natural fibre items.

The Whole Thing Catalogue
School Lane
Dunham Massey
Altrincham
Cheshire, WA14 5SZ
Telephone (061) 236 5116

A mixture of innovative products for the home and personal use, some green, some not quite so green, including vitamin and mineral supplements and numerous gadgets electrical and otherwise. Includes some wonderful and useful gift ideas.

PAINTS AND DIY PRODUCTS

AURO Organic Paints
See Saffron Building and Design Ltd below.

Crown/Berger
PO Box 37
Hollins Road
Darwen
Lancs, BB3 0BG

For more information about the ammonia- and formaldehyde-free eggshell paint, contact Crown at the above address.

LIVOS Natural Paint Products
27 Harvest Green
Newbury
Berkshire
RG14 6DW
Telephone (0635) 37988

LIVOS use plant chemistry to produce natural paints, waxes, wood preservatives and finishes, adhesives, putty, fillers, stain, lacquers and varnishes, thinners, cleaners, polish and natural art materials. All the products are non-toxic and completely natural. include ingredients such as plant oils, tree resins, herb extracts and beeswax and are all lead-free. The products used are those which affect the natural environment the least; for example, the resin for the oil-based products is obtained without felling trees, and any by-products are recycled whenever possible. LIVOS also produce a range of products for people who are highly sensitive even to natural plant derivatives such as certain resins, essential oils, alcohol etc. Contact the above address for a catalogue, price list and further information. The products are available by mail-order from LIVOS, from numerous outlets and also from The Whole Thing Catalogue and Green Farm Catalogue.

Saffron Building and Design Ltd
16 Church Street
Saffron Walden
Essex, CB10 1JW
Telephone (0799) 24744

This company imports over 100 different AURO organic paints and products for household use from Germany. The products are non-toxic and made entirely from natural ingredients. The range includes preservatives, varnishes, paints and cleaners. (Also available from The Whole Thing Catalogue.)

PET CARE

Rushall Organic Farms
The Manor
Upavon
Pewsey
Wilts

Rushall prepare their dog biscuits from organically grown crops produced on the farm. Contact them for a price list and details of delivery. Please send an SAE with your enquiry.

VITAMINS AND MINERALS

Bio Health Ltd
Culpeper Close
Medway City Estate
Rochester
Kent, ME2 4HU
Telephone (0634) 290115

Manufacturers and distributors of Purefil vitamins, minerals and herbs which are manufactured without extraneous tableting materials and contain only the active ingredients. Available from health stores, or contact Bio Health for stockist information in your area.

Green Farm Nutrition Centre
Burwash Common
Burwash
East Sussex, TN19 7LX
Telephone (0435) 882482

See under Mail Order (p.264) for more information.

Healthtec Nutrition Hotline
Telephone (0273) 620888

Free information about health, vitamins and minerals.

Vitahealth
PO Box 997
Rottingdean
Sussex, BN2 6WP

A wide range of pure supplements by mail order. Write for a catalogue/price list enclosing an SAE.

WATER FILTERS

Crystal Springs Ltd
The Clean Water Company
Freepost (BR813) Dept GS
Hove, BN3 2ZZ
Telephone (0273) 778161 (ask for Crystal Springs)

Effective counter-top and plumbed-in water filtration units. Very economical: one filter will produce the equivalent of three thousand 1 litre bottles of clean water. For more information please send an SAE to Crystal Springs with your enquiry.

Vertac Industries
Edison Road
St Ives
Cambridgeshire
Telephone (0480) 495757

Manufacture extremely efficient water filters that can be plumbed into the mains water supply. For more details contact Vertac.

WOOD

For the *Good Wood Guide*, write to Friends of the Earth, listed under 'Environment Groups' (p.293).

9

The Green Glossary and Fact Finder

Acetylcholine an enzyme which plays an important part in the transmission of nerve impulses.

Acetylcholinesterase an enzyme that stops the action of acetyl-choline.

Acid rain acidic rainfall which occurs as a result of a reaction between moisture in the atmosphere and gases such as sulphur dioxide and oxides of nitrogen released from vehicles, industry and power stations. The health of trees and woodland is threatened, and in cities buildings are being eroded. The effects of acid rain also have an impact on aquatic life and, in addition, drinking water supplies may be contaminated with aluminium because the acid rain causes aluminium to be liberated from soil and rocks in and around rivers, lakes and reservoirs. This has caused the death of fish, and birds feeding on water insects have also been affected.

Acute toxicity toxic effects which appear within a short time of a substance being absorbed.

Algae primitive microscopic plants, chiefly found in water. Algae lack true stems, roots and leaves but contain chlorophyll.

Alzheimer's disease a form of senile dementia or premature senility. It has been linked with aluminium intake from food and water.

Amines nitrogen-containing compounds formed when one or more hydrogen atoms has been replaced by a hydrocarbon radical. They can be considered ammonia derivatives.

Anticholinesterase agents substances which inhibit the action of **cholinesterase** (an enzyme which catalyses **acetylcholinesterase**). **Carbamate** insecticides and some **organophosphorus** insecticides are anticholinesterase agents.

Antimony metal used in some solders and matches. It is highly toxic if inhaled, and can also cause skin irritation.

Aplasia failure of a tissue or organ to develop normally.

Aplastic anaemia anaemia caused by **aplasia** of bone marrow or its destruction by chemical agents (e.g. benzene, arsenic) or by X-rays and other sources of ionizing radiation.

Aromatic compounds a term used to describe certain chemicals related to, and including, the solvent benzene. Others in the group include toluene and xylene.

Biocides sometimes known as 'broad spectrum treatments'. These substances kill a broad range of insects rather than one specific pest.

Biodegradable a substance that can be broken down in the environment by natural processes, and is harmlessly dispersed into the ecological cycle.

Borax dried sodium borate. It is found in crystal form in the great salt lakes of dry areas such as California, Nevada, Egypt and Iran.

Carbamates a category of insecticides some of which are **carcinogenic**, **teratogenic** and **mutagenic** and include bendiocarb, methiocarb (used in slug killers), and pirimicarb. They are **anticholinesterase agents**.

Carbon dioxide a combustion product of carbon. Most living creatures breathe out carbon dioxide.

Carcinogen/carcinogenic something that can stimulate the development of cancer, e.g. smoking, radiation, asbestos, some solvents, pesticides etc.

Chlorinated hydrocarbons a general term used to describe chemicals containing carbon linked directly to chlorine. They are fat soluble and include solvents such as trichloroethylene and numerous insecticides, including the infamous DDT and related compounds, chlordane and lindane. They are highly persistent in the soil (some DDT sprayed forty years ago is still active) and are not easily decomposed or broken down. They are a threat to wildlife and mammals, including ourselves.

Cholinesterase see **acetylcholinesterase**.

Chronic toxicity toxic effects which can develop slowly, and/or are due to a continuing or constant exposure to a toxic substance.

Cotton is grown with heavy use of pesticides, including DDT, and fertilizers. Even the seeds are treated with fungicides. Linen has a shorter growing cycle and receives fewer chemical applications during growth. Cotton and linen are also bleached, although it is possible to buy them unbleached in the UK. See under **formaldehyde** in the Data Sheets in Chapter 2 for more information about cotton treatments and alternatives.

Crocidolite blue asbestos.

Dioxins a group of 210 chemicals, 17 of which are considered to be dangerous. Of these, 2378-TCDD has been studied in detail and is extremely toxic. Dioxin is formed as a by-product of the manufacture of the herbicides 2,4,5-T and 2,4-D and agricultural chemicals. It also occurs as a result of chlorine bleaching and the combustion of chlorinated organic materials. Dioxins are present in many household paper products including paper towels, coffee filters, tampons and sanitary products, nappies, toilet paper, tea bags and milk cartons. These chemicals dissolve in oils and fats can migrate into fatty foods including milk, which can be a major source when packed in cardboard cartons. When taken into the body they accumulate in body fat and are released during dieting and pregnancy, the implications of which are unknown. Dioxins can cause chloracne, a severe skin rash, loss of the sense of taste and smell, depression and uncharacteristic bouts of anger. In animal studies they have been linked with genetic mutation, liver damage, and damage to the immune and nervous systems. There is some evidence that dioxins may also be **carcinogenic** and they are highly persistent in the environment. The Swedish National Chemical Inspectorate has recommended that personal hygiene products are not bleached with chlorine. Although the British Government does not recognize dioxin as a danger to health, it would be wise to seek alternatives. Use unbleached or non-chlorine bleached toilet paper and buy milk in glass bottles. If possible phase out tea bags and brew your tea in a teapot to avoid unnecessary exposure to dioxins.

Ecology the science of the relationship(s) between organisms and their environments or the study of the relationship between people and their environment.

EDTA (ethylene-diamine-tetra-acetate) a chemical used to prevent the brighteners and bleaching agents in washing powders from becoming active in storage. It acts in a similar way to **NTA** in the environment and biodegrades very slowly only in warm temperatures. EDTA and NTA form soluble compounds, with minerals and heavy metals triggering their entry into water and water supplies, and consequently the food chain. EDTA is also added to some foods during processing! In the same way that it binds with heavy metals, it binds with zinc, making it unavailable to the body.

Enzymes added to 'biological' washing powders to remove 'biological' stains which contain protein, such as blood, sweat, grass or chocolate. These **proteases** are mainly produced by the bacteria *Bacillus subtilis*. Enzymes do not differentiate between proteins from chocolate and those of the body, and as such they have a history of causing skin problems in consumers, and respiratory illness in people involved in their manufacture.

Ethanol   alcohol or ethyl alcohol synthesized by the fermentation of sugars and starches. It is widely used as a solvent, and is also in cleaning solutions and drugs. It is the intoxicating component of beer, wine and spirits and is highly flammable.

Eutrophication   an increase in the mineral and organic nutrients in a body of water, which encourages the abnormal growth of algae. This results in a drastic reduction of dissolved oxygen, creating an ecosystem which favours plant over animal life. Some species of algae release toxicants in order to eliminate other algae and this has been known to cause the death of large numbers of fish. The release of waste water (that contains phosphates from cleaning products and nitrates from farmland) into bodies of water is a directly causative factor. Another form of eutrophication may take place during the bacterial breakdown of organic (biodegradable) substances because this process also uses dissolved oxygen in the water.

Fragrance   can consist of any of up to four thousand different chemicals, most of which do not have to be listed on the product. Most are synthetic and are known to cause allergic reactions in sensitive people.

Gaia Hypothesis   Gaia is the Greek name for the Earth Goddess. The Gaia Hypothesis states that left to themselves, natural systems maintain their own balance and integrity through feedback loops – whereby both environment and organism have a cause and effect relationship with each other.

Greenhouse effect   a term applied to the potential effects of an increase in the concentration of so called 'greenhouse' gases, principally carbon dioxide from fossil fuel burning and deforestation, methane primarily from biological sources but also from landfill sites, **chlorofluorocarbons (CFCs)** and also nitrous oxide from the breakdown of fertilizers and combustion processes. There are about thirty greenhouse gases identified. Most greenhouse gases are naturally present in small amounts in the atmosphere and, together with water vapour, help to maintain the earth's tempera-
by trapping heat, much like the glass in a greenhouse. It is

the increase of these gases that has led to their build-up and the potential warming of the earth's temperature. The implications of global warming include changes in regional and seasonal weather patterns which would affect forestry and agriculture, elevated carbon dioxide levels unbalancing ecosystems, increased biological activity on ocean surface waters, and melting of glaciers increasing the volume of sea water and threatening low lying coastal areas.

Halon(s) a class of bromine containing chemicals similar to CFCs which contain chlorine (see Data Sheets in Chapter 2). Halons are used in some fire extinguishers. Some are inert and others are highly toxic. They are many times more destructive to the ozone layer than CFCs and it is thought that the two chemicals have a **synergistic** effect when combined in the upper atmosphere.

Hydrocarbons numerous organic compounds that consist of only carbon and hydrogen. They are flammable and some are **carcinogenic** and toxic. They may be used in mixtures or alone and include benzene, methane and toluene. Vehicles emit unburnt hydrocarbons which contribute to air pollution.

Imidazoline an ingredient in some air fresheners which acts by blocking the sense of smell.

Mercaptans various types of sulphur-containing organic compounds with an unpleasant odour. Methyl mercaptan is added to natural gas to make the detection of leaks possible. It is toxic.

Metabolism the system of physical and chemical changes that take place within an organism to produce energy and assimilate new material for repair and replacement of tissues.

Methaemoglobinaemia a condition of the blood which has been known to result from poisoning by nitrates, chlorates, ferricyanides, or after ingestion of oxidising drugs. It is potentially fatal and is especially dangerous to infants under three months.

Mutagen/mutagenic a substance/agent capable of causing heritable alterations in cells, genes and chromosomes of an organism. This process is known as mutation. Mutagens include radioactive elements, ultraviolet radiation, industrial wastes and certain chemicals.

Nitrates many fertilizers contain sodium or potassium nitrate and, although not toxic as such, the extensive use of nitrate fertilizers is causing them to appear in water supplies and contribute to **eutrophication** of bodies of water. Once inside the body, nitrates undergo chemical changes to become nitrites and then nitrous acid which combines with haemoglobin in the blood and reduces oxygen. This can cause fatigue, tiredness and sluggishness. In children this can produce **methaemoglobinaemia** leading to cyanosis, 'blue baby syndrome', and possibly to death. People who are anaemic are extremely susceptible to methaemoglobinaemia, as are people with low blood pressure. Nitrates also combine in the stomach with amines from items like beer, wine, tea, fish and cereals to form nitrosamines, which have been linked with the development of certain cancers. Sodium nitrate is added to foods like sausages, pork pies, ham and bacon to 'fix' the pink colour and inhibit bacterial growth. The other main sources are vegetables grown in soils treated with nitrate fertilizers and water supplies. Vitamin C offers some protection against nitrosamines, and teeth should be cleaned after each meal as bacteria in the mouth contribute to the production of nitrites from nitrates. Drink filtered or bottled spring water and eat organically grown vegetables whenever possible.

Nitrosamines see **nitrates.**

NTA (nitrilo-tri-acetic acid) in the early 1980s this chemical was introduced as a replacement for phosphates in washing powders. It has been established as a carcinogenic agent with teratogenic properties and is banned in a number of countries; parliamentary procedures are under way to ban it in the UK. It acts in the environment in a similar way to **EDTA**, but is slightly ᴬsier to biodegrade.

Optical brighteners are harmful substances added to some washing powders, but may also be found in paper and toothpaste. They belong to the stilbene and tyro group of derivatives. They attach to fabrics during washing and convert invisible ultraviolet light into visible 'blue' light creating a fluorescence which makes the garment appear 'whiter than white'. They may cause allergic skin reactions in sensitive people, especially if in contact with the skin in the presence of sunlight. They are difficult to biodegrade, and accumulate in plant roots and the intestines of fish.

Organic substances based on carbon, apart from a few inorganic gases and carbonates. Organic farming means farming without artificial fertilizers or pesticides.

Organochlorines include liquid solvents, many pesticides, PVC and PCB found in electrical equipment and some plastics. Organochlorines are highly toxic and **carcinogenic**, and organochlorines in cleaning solvents may accumulate in the body and cause damage to the organs, especially the liver and kidneys. Sources of organochlorines include pesticides, dry-cleaning fluids, wood preservatives, cleaning products, plastic and paint vapours, chlorine and industrial emissions.

Organophosphorus compounds phosphorus-incorporated organic compounds. They are **anticholinesterase agents** and include many household insecticides including chlorpyrifos, diazinon, dimethoate and fenitrothion. Some organophosphorus compounds have been used in warfare due to their anticholinesterase action on the nervous system.

Oxidizing agent a chemical which accelerates fire. When heated it may explode.

Ozone a blue, gaseous form of oxygen. It is formed naturally from diatomic oxygen by exposure to ultraviolet light. In the upper atmosphere the **ozone layer** protects the earth from the sun's more damaging ultraviolet rays, but at ground level ozone can be unhealthy (see Chapter 2). Levels of ozone are highest in towns with a high traffic level on hot, sunny days.

Ozone layer also called the ozonosphere, a concentrated layer of **ozone** in the upper atmosphere. The ozonosphere absorbs dangerous ultraviolet radiation from the sun, but is being destroyed by reactions in the upper atmosphere between chlorine- and bromine-containing compounds which are not destroyed in the lower atmosphere, primarily **CFCs** and **Halons**.

PAHs see **polycyclic aromatic hydrocarbons.**

PCBs see **polychlorinated biphenyls.**

Phenols used in the synthesis of plastic resins and wood preservatives. They are derived from coal tar or petroleum and include carbolic acid (a disinfectant), creosote and PCP (pentachlorophenol).

Phosgene a highly poisonous gas emitted from the burning of certain chemicals and used in chemical warfare.

Phosphates some washing powders still contain these chemicals and they are also found in dishwasher powders, some wool washing agents, scouring powders and some multi-purpose cleaners. They are added to soften water, stabilize acidity and contribute to the cleaning power of the product. Phosphates are responsible for a process known as **eutrophication** in water ecosystems.

Polycarboxylates are a relatively new replacement for phosphates in washing powders. They are petroleum based with a structure similar to some acrylics and plastics and are almost non-biodegradable. Very little is known, as yet, of their effects on the environment, humans and animals.

Polychlorinated biphenyls (PCBs) a group of industrial compounds which are highly toxic and persistent in the environment. The death of seals in the North Sea has been linked with their ingestion of chemicals, including PCBs, which infiltrate the food chain and build up in fatty tissue. Chronic exposure to PCBs can ~se severe skin rashes, damage to the glandular system and interfere with liver function; they are also suspected carcinogens. PCBs appear on the Government's 'Red List' of substances subject to stricter controls for both direct and indirect discharges to water. They also appear on the EC List I 'Black List'.

Polycyclic aromatic hydrocarbons (PAHs)   chemicals found in tars and formed during incomplete combustion of numerous complex organic chemicals. Vehicles may emit PAHs if badly tuned, and the group contains numerous chemicals that are the constituents of smoke.

Propellant   a compressed gas (originally CFCs – chlorofluoro-carbons – now more likely to be butane) which causes the release of the product in an aerosol can when the button is pressed.

Proteases   protein degrading **enzymes**.

Sick Building Syndrome   a collection of symptoms, now officially recognized by the World Health Organization, caused by people's reactions to a combination of factors in certain buildings. The causes include environmental stressors, poor ventilation, chemicals, lighting problems, ducted heating systems and lack of control over the environment.

Surfacant, petroleum based   (surface active agents) the main cleaning ingredient (detergent) in a wide range of cleaning products. They separate dirt containing fats and oils from the surface being cleaned and keep them suspended in the washing water. During the manufacture of surfacants, non-biodegradable impurities are formed which are toxic to fish and accumulate in the environment. Surfacants have a low biodegradability, and some form **carcinogenic** and **teratogenic** compounds during degradation.

Synergistic   the combined action of two or more substances to achieve an effect greater than the sum of their individual effects.

Systemic   affecting the whole system rather than isolated parts.

Tecnazene   a fumigant chemical used to stop potatoes sprouting during storage. It is a possible animal **carcinogen** and is persistent in the environment.

TCDD   see **dioxin**.

Teratogenic   an agent that induces abnormalities and/or birth defects in a developing foetus. These include thalidomide, exposure to radiation and some pesticides.

Vegetable-based detergents   detergents derived from coconut or palm oils. These are renewable and biodegradable.

Warfarin   in medicine, used as an anticoagulant drug to prevent blood clotting, also used as a rat poison.

Washing powders, biological   contain **enzymes** which degrade proteins.

Volatile organic compounds   substances from petrochemicals or synthetic alcohol, including some toluene, propane, benzene and butane. Some are depressants, some **carcinogenic**. Found in cleaning solvents, polishes, paints, plastics, scents.

Weighted silk   silk which is treated with salts of tin and lead to make it heavier.

Xenobiotics   chemicals that are foreign to the body.

Sources

CHAPTER 1

Bertschler, J., et al., Psychological components of environmental illness: factor analysis of changes during treatment, *Clinical Ecology*, vol. III, no. 2, pp. 85–94

Breysse, P.A., The health cost of tight homes, *Journal of the American Medical Association* 245, 1981, pp. 267–8

Crinnion, W., Brief review of neurotoxic effects of environmental chemicals, Townsend Letter 59, June 1988, pp. 256–8

Is your environment making you ill? Environmental health hazards, *Which?* April 1989, pp. 29–32

Finnegan, M.J., Pickering, C.A.C., & Burge, P.S., Sick Building Syndrome: prevalence studies, *British Medical Journal* 289, 1984, pp. 1573–5

Fletcher, D., Sick Building Syndrome, a study of 4373 office workers, Ann. Occup. Hyg., vol. 31, 1987, pp. 493–504

Forsman, S., Health hazards associated with the introduction of new chemicals in industry, Organization of Public Health in Europe 8, Health and the Environment 1977, pp. 124–9

Health aspects related to indoor air quality: report on a WHO working group, WHO Regional Office for Europe 1979, Copenhagen, Euro Reports and Studies 21

Indoor air pollutants: exposure and health effects: report on a WHO meeting 1982, Euro Reports and Studies 78

Laseter, J.L., et al., Chlorinated hydrocarbon pesticides in environmentally sensitive patients, *Clinical Ecology*, vol. II, no. 1, 1983, pp. 3–12

Levin, H., Indoor air pollution: the environment moves indoors, *ASTM Standardization News*, December 1988, pp. 34–8

Lewis, R.G., & Wallace, L.A., Toxic organic vapours in indoor air, *ASTM Standardization News*, December 1988, pp. 40–44

Mercury pesticide figures: The Statistical Abstract of the United States 1976

Moschandreas, D.J., et al., Indoor air pollution in the residential environment, US Environmental Protection Agency 1978, Document EPA-600/7-78-229

Pollution begins at home, *New Scientist*, 5 December 1985, pp. 34–7

Randolph, T.G., Depressions caused by home exposures to gas and combustion products of gas, oil, coal, *Journal of Laboratory and Clinical Medicine* 46, 1955, pp. 198–224

Rea, W.J., et al., Pesticides and brain-function changes in a controlled environment, *Clinical Ecology*, vol. II, no. 3, 1984, pp. 145–50

Robinson, A.S., Burge, P.S., et al., Comparison of health problems related to work and environmental measurements in 2 office buidings with different ventilation systems, *British Medical Journal* 291, 10 August 1985, pp. 373–6

Sykes, J.M., Sick Building Syndrome: a review, Specialist Inspector Reports 10: Health and Safety Executive, Technology Division

The lungs and the environment, *Respiratory Disease in Practice*, vol. 6, no. 3, June/July 1989, p. 7

US Environmental Protection Agency, Washington, DC

Which? Way to Health, August 1989

Yanchinksi, S., New analysis links dioxin to cancer, *New Scientist*, 28 October 1989, p. 24

CHAPTER 2

1990 Pollution Handbook, National Society for Clean Air

Ames, B., Dietary carcinogens and anticarcinogens: oxygen radicals and degenerative diseases, *Science*, 221, 1983, pp. 1256–63

Ammonia: IPC's international programme on chemical safety, Environmental Health Criteria 54, WHO, Geneva, 1986

Beisel, W.R., Single nutrient effects on immulogic functions, *Journal of the American Medical Association* 245, 2 January 1981, pp. 53–8

Bryce-Smith, D., & Waldron, H.A., Lead behaviour and criminality, *The Ecologist* 4, 1974, p. 10

Calabrese, E., et al., Influence of dietary vitamin E on susceptibility to ozone exposure, Bulletin of Environmental Contamination and Toxicology 34, 1985, pp. 417–22

Chaitow, L., *Amino Acids in Therapy*, Thorsons, 1985

Chandra, R.K., Immunodeficiency in undernutrition and overnutrition, *Nutrition Reviews* vol. 39, no. 6, 1981, pp. 225–31

Chlordane: Consumer Information, US Environmental Protection Agency Office of Pesticides and Toxic Substances, Washington, DC, ̄ust 1987

Citizen's Guide to Pesticides, US Environmental Protection Agency Office of Pesticides and Toxic Substances, September 1987

Connor, S., Wall coating highly toxic at very high temperatures, *Daily Telegraph*, 30 June 1989

Control of substances hazardous to health and Control of carcinogenic substances, Health and Safety Commission

Crinnion, W., Brief review of neurotoxic effects of environmental chemicals, Townsend Letter 59, June 1988 pp. 256–8

Dormandy, T.L., Free radical oxidation and antioxidants, *Lancet* 1, 1988, pp. 647–8

Environmental Protection Agency Health Advisory Summaries on pesticides, wood preservatives, herbicides, etc.

Fluoride and fluorides: IPC's International Programme on Chemical Safety Environmental Health Criteria 36

Formaldehyde: an assessment of its health effects, National Research Council Committee on Toxicology 1980, National Academy of Sciences, Washington, DC

Gammage, R.B., & Kaye, S.V., *Indoor Human Air and Health*, Lewis Publishers Inc.

Goldsmith, J.R., Comparative epidemiology of men exposed to asbestos and man-made mineral fibre, *American Journal of Industrial Medicine* 10, 1986, pp. 543–52

Goldstein, PABA, Protection against ozone toxicity, Ach. Environ. Health, 1972

Gross, R.I., & Newberne, P.L., Role of nutrition in immunologic function, *Physiologic Reviews* 60, January 1980, pp. 188–302

Hallowell, C.D., & Mikach, R.R., Sources and concentrations of organic compounds in indoor environments, Bulletin Y.Y. Acad. Med. vol. 57, no. 181, pp. 962–77

Hazardous Building Materials: A guide to the selection of alternatives, E. & F.N. Spon, London, 1986

Health aspects related to indoor air quality: report on a WHO working group, WHO Regional Office for Europe 1979, Copenhagen, Euro Reports and Studies 21

Indoor air pollutants: exposure and health effects: report on a WHO meeting 1982, Euro Reports and Studies 78

Irving Sax, N., & Lewis, R.J., *Dangerous Properties of Industrial Materials*, (7th edn.) Van Nostrand Rheinhold, New York, 1989

Lead or health?, report of the Conservation Society Pollution Working Party

Levin, H., Indoor air pollution, *ASTM Standardization News*, December 1988, pp. 34–8

Lewis, R.R., & Wallace, L.A., Toxic organic vapours in indoor air, *ASTM Standardization News*, December 1988, pp. 40–44

Martlew, G., & Silver, S., *Stay Well in Winter*, Thorsons, 1989

Martlew, G., & Silver, S., *The Medicine Chest*, Thorsons, 1988

Mellanby, K., *Pesticides and Pollution*, Fontana, 1972

Milner, J.A., Dietary antioxidants and cancer, *Contemporary Nutrition*, October 1985

Moschandreas, D.J., et al., Indoor air pollution in the residential environment, US Environmental Protection Agency 1978, Document EPA-600/7-78-229

Nam, K., & Gracey, D.R., Talcum powder and children, *American Journal of Diseases in Children*, vol. III, June 1966, pp. 653–4

National Research Council Report, Washington National Academy Press, 1982

Neeleman et al., Deficits in psychologic and classroom performance of children with elevated dentine lead levels, *New England Journal of Medicine* 300, 1979, pp. 689–95

Nero, A., Controlling indoor pollution, *Scientific American*, vol. 258, 5 May 1988

New analysis links dioxin to cancer, *New Scientist*, 28 October 1989, p. 24

Omenn, G., A double-blind randomized trial with beta carotene and retinol in persons at high risk of lung cancer due to occupational asbestos exposures and/or cigarette smoking, Publ. Heal R. 16, 1988, pp. 99–125

Paraquat and Diquat: IPC's International Programme on Chemical Safety Environmental Health Criteria 39, WHO, Geneva, 1984

Pollution begins at home, *New Scientist*, 5 December 1985, pp. 34–7

Porter, J.A.H., Acute respiratory distress following formalin inhalation, *Lancet* 2, 1975, pp. 603–4

Public Health Risks of Exposure to Asbestos (published for the Commission of the European Communities), Pergamon Press, 1977

Recognition and management of pesticide poisonings, US Environmental Protection Agency, EPA-540/9-88-001, March 1989, 4th edn.

Report to Congress on Indoor Air Quality, vol. 1: Federal programs addressing indoor air quality, US Environmental Protection ^ y, EPA-400/1-89-001B, August 1989

Congress on Indoor Air Quality, vol. 2: Assessment and of indoor air pollution, US Environmental Protection EPA-400/1-89-001C, August 1989

Congress on Indoor Air Quality, vol. 3: Indoor air pollution research needs statement, US Environmental Protection Agency, EPA-400/1-89-001D, August 1989

Report to Congress on Indoor Air Quality: Executive summary and recommendations, US Environmental Protection Agency, EPA-400/1-89-001A, August 1989

Rockville, Tabershaw Occupational Medicine Association P.A.

Rostenberg, A.J., Bairstow, B., & Luther, T.W., A study of exzematous sensitivity to formaldehyde, *Journal of Investigative Dermatology* 19, 1952, pp. 459–62

Salonen, J.T., et al., Vitamin E and selenium blood levels and cancer incidence, *British Medical Journal* 290, 9 February 1985, pp. 417–20

Serum beta carotene, vitamins A and E, selenium and risk of lung cancer, *New England Journal of Medicine*, 13 November 1986

Shamberger, Baughman, Kalchert, Wills & Hoffman, Carcinogen induced chromosomal breakage decreased by antioxidants, Proc. Nat. Acad. Sci. USA 5, May 1983, p. 1461

Shekelle, Vitamin A and beta carotene protect human lungs against cigarette smoke, *Lancet*, 28 November 1981

Sick Building Syndrome, IBC Technical Services in conjunction with CWA Information and Research Ltd

Simons, P., Getting to the glass roots of cancer, *New Scientist* 1447, October 1985

Spizer, F.E., et al., Palpitation rate associated with fluorocarbon exposure in a hospital setting, *New England Journal of Medicine* vol. 292, no. 624, 1975

Tabershaw, I.R., Doyle, H.N., et al., A review of the formaldehyde problems in mobile homes, report to National Particleboard Association

Taylor, G.S., & Hern, W.S., Cardiac arrhythmias to aerosol propellants, *Journal of the American Medical Association* vol. 219, no. 8, 1970

Termiticides: Consumer Information, US Environmental Protection Agency, Washington, DC, Document OPA-87-014

Trace elements in human health and disease, Symposium report

Turid, I., *Indoor Air Quality and Human Health*, Stanford University Press, 1988

Wald, N., Thompson, S., Densem, J., et al., Serum beta carotene and subsequent risk of cancer, *British Journal of Cancer* 57, 1988, pp. 428–33

Wayne, L.B., Bryan, R.J., & Ziedman, K., Irritant effects of industrial chemicals: formaldehyde, DHEW (National Institute of Occupational Safety and Health) Publication no. 77–177, US Govt Printing Office, Washington, DC

Willet, W.C., et al., Blood selenium levels and cancer rates, *Lancet*, 16 July 1983, pp. 130–34

Wills, G.C., Influence of ascorbic acid upon the liver, Canad. M.A.J. 76, 1957, p. 1047

World Health Organization, Environmental Health 26

CHAPTER 3

Foliage plants for removing indoor air pollutants from energy efficient homes, National Research Council 1980, 1981, a,b

Functional uses of indoor plants in the workplace, Landscape Services Property Management Division, Alberta Public Works

Indoor air pollutants: exposure and health effects, Report on WHO meeting, Copenhagen, June 1982

Lighting Research and Technology, vol. 21, no. 1, 1989, Chartered Institution of Building Services Engineers

Martlew, G., & Silver, S., *Stay Well in Winter*, Thorsons, 1989

Ott, J., *Health and Light*, Devin-Adair Co., USA, 1973

Robertson, A.S., McInnes, M., et al., Building sickness: are symptoms related to the office lighting? Ann. Occup. Hyg. vol. 33, no. 1, 1989, pp. 47–59

Wolverton, B.C., Space bio-technology in housing, NASA National Space Technology Laboratories (paper presented at the National Association of Home Builders Convention, Dallas, Texas, 19 January 1986)

Wolverton, B.C., McDonald, R.C., & Watkins, E.A., Foliage plants for removing indoor air pollutants from energy-efficient homes, Ec. Bot. vol. 38, no. 2, 1984, pp. 224–8

Wolverton, B.C., McDonald, R.C., & Mesick, H.H., Foliage plants for the indoor removal of the primary combustion gases carbon monoxide and nitrogen dioxide, *Journal of the Mississippi Academy of Sciences* vol. 30, pp. 1–8

CHAPTER 4

All Mu~~ch~~ and Magic, Henry Doubleday Research Association

~~na~~tural Pest and Disease Control, Century, 1987

~~Veg~~etables Naturally, Century, 1985

Grow More Vegetables, Berkeley Ten Speed Press,

The Quantum Carrot, Ebury, 1987

Pesticide exceeds limit in Yorkshire rivers, *New Scientist* 3, April 1986

Pesticides: an unhealthy dependence? *Science* 85, October, p. 14

Temple, J., *Gardening Without Chemicals*, Thorsons, 1986

US Environmental Protection Agency advisory summaries on specific pesticides

Wright, M., (Ed.) *Britain's Wildlife, Plants and Flowers*, Reader's Digest, 1987

CHAPTER 5

ASTM Standardization News, December 1988, pp. 34—8

Bertschler, J., et al., Psychological components of environmental illness: factor analysis of changes during treatment, *Clinical Ecology*, vol. III, no. 2, pp. 85—94

Breysse, P.A., The health cost of tight homes, *Journal of the American Medical Association* 245, 1981, pp. 267—8

Burge, S., & Hedge, A., Sick Building Syndrome: a study of 4373 office workers, Ann. Occup. Hyg., vol. 31, 1987, pp. 493—504

Clinical Ecology, vol. III, no. 2

Crinnion, W., Brief review of neurotoxic effects of environmental chemicals, Townsend Letter 59, June 1988, pp. 256—8

Finnegan, M.J., Pickering, C.A.C., & Burge, P.S., Sick Building Syndrome: prevalence studies, *British Medical Journal* 289, 1984, pp. 1573—5

Fletcher, C., Sick Building Syndrome and days off linked, *Daily Telegraph*, 30 June 1989

Health aspects related to indoor air quality: report on a WHO working group, WHO Regional Office for Europe 1979, Copenhagen, Euro Reports and Studies 21

Indoor air pollutants: exposure and health effects, report on a WHO meeting 1982, Euro Reports and Studies 78

Is your environment making you ill? Environmental Health Hazards, *Which?*, April 1989, pp. 29—32

King, D.S., Can allergic exposure provoke psychological symptoms? A double-blind test, *Biological Psychiatry*, vol. 16, no. 1, 1981, pp. 3—19

Laseter, J.L., et al., Chlorinated hydrocarbon pesticides in environmentally sensitive patients, *Clinical Ecology*, vol. II, no. 1, 1983, pp. 3—12

Levin, H., Indoor air pollution: the environment moves indoors

Mandell, M., Cerebral reactions in allergic patients, (paper presented at the second International Congress of Social Psychiatry, London, 1969)

Mandell, M., Mould allergy as a major cause of bio-ecological mental illness, In L. Dickey (Ed.), *Clinical Ecology*, 1976

Moschandreas, D.J., et al., Indoor air pollution in the residential environment, US Environmental Protection Agency 1978, Document EPA-600/7-78-229

Pollution begins at home, *New Scientist*, 5 December 1985, pp. 34–7

Rea, W.J., et al., Pesticides and brain-function changes in a controlled environment, *Clinical Ecology*, vol. II, no. 3, 1984, pp. 145–50

Randolph, T.G., Depressions caused by home exposures to gas and combustion products of gas, oil and coal, *Journal of Laboratory and Clinical Medicine* 46, 1955, pp. 198–224

Robinson, A.S., Burge, P.S., et al., Comparison of health problems related to work and environmental measurements in 2 office buildings with different ventilation systems, *British Medical Journal*, 10 August 1985, pp. 373–6

Sykes, J.M., Sick Building Syndrome: a review, Specialist Inspector Reports 10, Health and Safety Executive, Technology Division

CHAPTER 6

Becker, R., *The Body Electric*, William Morris, USA, 1985

Becker, R., *Cross Currents*, Jeremy P. Tarcher, USA, 1990

Caufield, C., *Multiple Exposures*, Secker & Warburg, 1989

A Citizen's Guide to Radon, US Environmental Protection Agency, Washington, DC, 1986

Clarke, R.H., & Southwood, T.R., Risks from ionizing radiation, *Nature* 338, 1989, p. 197

Gordon, R., *Are You Sleeping in a Safe Place?*, Dulwich Health Society

Graves, T., *Needles of Stone*, Turnstone Press, 1978

The Householder's Guide to Radon, Department of the Environment, Central Office of Information, HMSO, 1988

How much do a few hertz hurt?, *The Economist*, 16 April 1988

Living with Radiation, National Radiological Protection Board, 1988

Martlew, G., & Silver, S., *Stay Well in Winter*, Thorsons, 1989

National Radiological Protection Board documents, including 'Board statement on radon in homes', NRPB, vol. 1, no. 1, 1990

N   Power Lines Project Report papers, New York Dept of

                and childhood leukaemia, *British Medical Journal*, 1
             988, p. 804; *Journal of the American Medical Association*,
             y 1988, p. 1131; *Lancet*, 6 February 1988, p. 272

Radon in Houses, Department of the Environment, Central Office of Information, HMSO, 1987

Radon reduction in new construction: an interim guide, US Environmental Protection Agency, Washington, DC, 1987

Radon reduction methods, US Environmental Protection Agency, Washington, DC, 1987

Smith, C., & Best, S., *Electromagnetic Man*, Dent, 1990

Underwood, G., *Pattern of the Past*, Abacus, 1972

von Pohl, G.F., *Earth Currents*, Frech-Verlag, Stuttgart, 1987

CHAPTER 7

Abdullah, T., et al., Garlic review, *Journal of the National Medical Association*, vol. 80, no. 4, 88, pp. 439–45

Algae as sources of lysine and theonine in supplementing wheat or bread diets, *Science* 124, 1956, pp. 536–7

Ames, B., Dietary carcinogens and anticarcinogens: oxygen radicals and degenerative diseases, *Science* 221, 1983, pp. 1256–63

Beisel, W.R., Single nutrient effects on immulogic functions, *Journal of the American Medical Association*, 2 Janury 1981, pp. 53–8

Bertschler, J., et al., Psychological components of Environmental Illness: factor analysis of changes during treatment, *Clinical Ecology*, vol. III, no. 2, pp. 85–94

Calabrese, E., et al., Influence of dietary vitamin E on susceptibility to ozone exposure, *Bulletin of Environmental Contamination and Toxicology* 34, 1985, pp. 417–22

Chaitow, L., *Amino Acids in Therapy*, Thorsons, 1985

Chakraborty, D., et al., Biochemical studies on polychlorinated biphenyl toxicity in rats: manipulation by vitamin C, *International Journal of Vitamin Nutrition Research* 48, pp. 22–3, 1978

Chandra, R.K., Immunodeficiency in undernutrition and overnutrition, *Nutrition Review* vol. 39, no. 6, 1981, pp. 225–31

DiLuzio, N.R., The employment of antioxidants in the prevention and treatment of experimentally induced liver injury, *Progressive Biochemical Pharmacological* 5, 1967, pp. 325–42

Dormandy, T.L., Free radical oxidation and antioxidants, *Lancet* 1, 1978, pp. 647–48

Gross, R.I., & Newberne, P.L., Role of nutrition in immunologic function, *Physiologic Reviews* 60, January 1980, pp. 188–302

Laseter, J.L., et al., Chlorinated hydrocarbon pesticides in environmentally sensitive patients, *Clinical Ecology* vol. II, no. 1, 1983, pp. 3–12

Lead and thiamine, *Toxicology and Applied Pharmacology* 16, June 1981

Marsa, L., Oxygen: is it the death of us? New light on the 'free radicals' that cause aging, *Los Angeles Times*, 28 August 1989

Martlew, G., & Silver, S., *Stay Well in Winter*, Thorsons, 1989

Martlew, G., & Silver, S., *The Medicine Chest*, Thorsons, 1988

Martlew, G., & Silver, S., *The Pill Protection Plan*, Thorsons, 1988

Milner, H., Algae as food, *Scientific American*, October 1953, pp. 31–5

Milner, J.A., Dietary antioxidants and cancer, *Contemporary Nutrition*, October 1985

O'Banion, D., *An Ecological and Nutritional Approach to Behaviour Medicine*, Charles C. Thomas, London, 1976

Oberly, L.W., & T.D., Free radicals, cancer and ageing, Mod Ageing Res, vol. 8, 1986, pp. 325–71

Omenn, G., A double-blind randomized trial with beta carotene and retinol in persons at high risk of lung cancer due to occupational asbestos exposures and/or cigarette smoking, *Public Health Reviews* 16, 1988, pp. 99–125

Oxygen radicals and tissue destruction in influenza, *Hospital Practice*, 15 August 1989

Pheiffer, C., *Mental and Elemental Nutrients*, Keats, 1975

Pore, R.S., Detoxification of chlordecone poisoned rats with chlorella and chlorella derived sporopollenin, *Drug and Chemical Toxicology*, vol. 7, no. 1, 1984, pp. 57–71

Randolph, T.G., Depressions caused by home exposures to gas and combustion products of gas, oil and coal, *Journal of Laboratory and Clinical Medicine* 46, 1955, pp. 198–224

Rea, W.J., et al., Pesticides and brain-function changes in a controlled environment, *Clinical Ecology*, vol. II, no. 3, 1984, pp. 145–50

Reich, R., Royce, L., & Martin, G., Eicosapentanoic acid reduces the invasive and metastatic activities of malignant tumor cells, *Biochemical and Biophysical Research Communications* 160, 1989, pp. 559–64

Robinson, R.K., & Guzman-Juarez, M., The nutritional potential of the algae, *UK Plant Foods for Man*, University of Reading, 1978

Schrare, C.W., et al., Evaluation of detoxification regimen for fat stored xenobiotics, *Medical Hypothesis* 9, 1982, pp. 265–82

⁀erum beta carotene, vitamins A and E, selenium and risk of lung ⁀ncer, *New England Journal of Medicine*, 13 November 1986

⁀rger, Baughman, Kalchert, Wills & Hoffman, Carcinogen-
⁀hromosomal breakage decreased by antioxidants, Proc.
⁀ci. USA 5, May 1983, p. 1461

⁀ A and beta carotene protect human lungs against

Index